Date Due

NO 6 32			
Dee 18			
DE 28			
AP 28 70			
AP 16 71			
CF.			
APR 22 1982			
	PRINTED	IN U. S. A.	

TRENDS IN SCIENCE

VOLUME 1

Editor: George A. Baitsell

THE WORLD OF THE

ELECTRON MICROSCOPE

by Ralph W. G. Wyckoff

New Haven: YALE UNIVERSITY PRESS, 1958

FOREWORD

THIS VOLUME is the first in a new series, to be called Trends in Science, which has been rendered possible by a fortunate circumstance. Many of the scientists who have participated in the major discoveries that have made the first half of the twentieth century so notable are still active in their laboratory research and university duties. Their knowledge of past and present progress qualifies them as few others could be to assay future developments. In the Trends in Science volumes these leaders in scientific research interpret their own field for the benefit of general readers and also for the new generation of investigators who are forwarding the quest for knowledge.

Each writer will describe the situation in his specialty as it was around the beginning of the century, as it is at present, and as it may be in the years ahead. The contributors to the series, it is expected, will also present some of their material as a lecture under the auspices of the Yale Chapter of the Society of Sigma Xi.

The World of the Electron Microscope by R. W. G. Wyckoff is concerned with discoveries in the field of the infinitely minute particles, such as the virus of polio and a multitude of other particles which hold the key to knowledge of the structure of lifeless matter and also of every living organism. The author began his research career at Cornell University and continued in positions of increasing importance. He has been associated with the Carnegie Institution of Washington, the University of Michigan, and the Rockefeller Institute for Medical Research, was from 1952 to 1954 science attaché at the American Embassy in London, and now holds a major research position at the National Institutes of Health. His numerous published research contributions in the fields of physics and biology have brought him world-wide recognition and membership in many learned societies, including the National Academy of Sciences.

GEORGE A. BAITSELL

PREFACE

THIS SHORT BOOK is an expansion of a lecture delivered in 1956 before the Yale Chapter of Sigma Xi. It has not been written for specialists in the field with which it deals. Instead it has as its object a brief description of electron microscopy and related electron optical techniques for other scientists and for nonscientists who are interested in following the general unfolding of our knowledge of nature and especially in gaining through a specific example some insight into the steps by which this proceeds. It seeks to present in scientific but nontechnical language this limited though vigorously growing field in such a form as to give a valid idea of the sorts of problem currently being studied, of the general way in which these problems are being approached, of their significance for and place within the wider reach of natural science, and of the broad directions of future development.

It has two claims to inclusion within a series entitled Trends in Science. As an attempt by an active worker to explain to others what he and his fellows are doing and why, it represents what ought to be a trend in science. As an account of the diverse uses to which a new instrument has been put, it draws attention to a type of specialization which is serving more and more as the channel for present-day research. Such a description of the scope and methods of a typical specialty may illumine and help to clarify some of the genuinely serious issues inherent in the prevailing trend it illustrates.

There is a growing need for the scientist to try to interpret his work and its goals to a society increasingly aware that what he does is altering the guiding principles and not merely the machinery of its daily life. The techniques of popularized science are already developed to the point of giving the layman a daily account of both the newly found facts of science and what some workers in laboratories hope will turn out to be facts. This is interesting but unimportant. The facts of science, new and old, determine the technological progress of our culture, but the changes in man's ways of thinking brought about by the growth of science are having a decisive influence on the course of human development. To understand the special character of scientific thought we need examples of how it formulates its problems and goes about their solution. It is thus not sufficient that what society knows of the study of nature should be derived from the journalist with his urge to dramatize facts and personalities. Direct communication between scientist and nonscientist is not and cannot be easy. It demands a genuine effort on the part of each. The scientist cannot make his approach to nature clear to others unless he tries to express himself with a minimum reliance on his specialized jargon; and the nonscientist will always have a false picture of how science progresses unless he is willing to learn some of the technical terms required for scientific precision.

Brilliant discoveries and new insights into nature give vital direction to future investigation and integrated expression to what has already been learned, but it is not through them that science has principally advanced. On the contrary, sound natural knowledge grows through a mass of toil that is as often crowded with failure and boresomely devoted to the solution of small problems as are man's other efforts to create. The nonscientist who wishes to see science as it is and to appreciate how it is transforming his world must be prepared to learn of it through these details which are its life's blood.

The following description of electron microscopy makes use of such details to outline the new picture this instrument has given of the submicroscopic texture of matter. In order to comprehend this picture it is necessary to know something of what an electron lens is and what actually happens when electrons and matter meet; an appreciation of these physical principles is essential to an understanding of the successes of this new tool and of the reasons for its failures. In penetrating a new realm of nature the scientist is largely the slave of the little he already knows about it. This explains why progress in electron microscopy has been so dependent on improvements, which often must seem trivial, in the ways he prepares his specimens. Without understanding the specific nature of these improvements one cannot realize how they extend our possibilities of learning more, and one cannot see why the path of development has been what it is.

The growth of this special field of research has not been unique, and the person who is ready to follow its details will gain a feeling of the way science actually progresses. He will see how the solution of a succession of small problems properly chosen contributes to a larger objective; and he will genuinely grasp the fact that scientific, like other, progress is sound only if the underlying work is well done, and significant only when directed toward questions about nature that are basic as well as real. What is written, whether technical or nontechnical, should reflect both these aspects of good scientific work; and this discussion of electron microscopy seeks to show how, in dealing with a wide variety of specific problems, it is defining and solving questions of general significance to our understanding of the material world.

Electron microscopy is representative of the specialties through which more and more of our research into nature is being conducted. Like many of these it concentrates on applying a single group of experimental techniques to numerous superficially unrelated problems. This contrasts with the form of research which brings several different techniques to bear on a single problem that usually falls within the sphere of one of the basic divisions of science. There is a widespread tendency to condemn specialties built around instruments as an evil against which we should all struggle. This is a false as well as a futile attitude. Specialization in research is made inevitable by the complexity of our experiments and ensures that expertness which is essential to all good work. This does not of course mean that there are no dangers in the present rapid trend. Nevertheless a good experimentalist can now rarely escape being a specialist, and under present conditions few can master several techniques.

It follows that the growth of specialization is a danger mainly to those who are not specially trained in anything and to those who are content with mere technical proficiency. There is a tendency to imagine that one can escape the need to be expert in the use of specialized equipment by employing a technician to maintain and make observations with it. This is unfortunate from the standpoint both of the scientist who thereby loses the necessary intimacy with his experimental material and of the technician whose lack of a disciplined knowledge of what he examines prevents recognition of the unusual when he sees it. "Team research," now so popular, replaces the nonspecialist and his technicians with two or more specialists in different fields. It is a useful way to carry out the so-called project research which seeks attainable answers to clearly defined questions but it is not a substitute for a trained and creative individual.

Specialties are thought to be narrowing not only because they are easily confounded with techniques but because the attempt is frequently made to partition them among several sciences. Seen from any one of the basic sciences, electron microscopy or any other specialty based on instrumentation is of limited interest—and taught from such a limited standpoint it must indeed be narrowing and inadequate. Nevertheless, as the following discussion will demonstrate, a specialty can range widely over the totality of natural knowledge. The real problem is thus an educational one. A practical way must be found to train workers already mature and experienced in the basic sciences so that they can develop the growing specialty wherever it may lead.

CONTENTS

ILLUSTRATIONS

Plates between pp. 60 and 61

xiii

Chapter 1 | INTRODUCTION

ELECTRON MICROSCOPY should be considered as part of man's unending efforts to see, with ever better clarity and in increasing detail, the material world in which he lives and of which he forms so small a part. As such it is the present most active phase of that direct examination into the fine structure of matter which began in the seventeenth century with the construction of the first microscopes.

Each of us consciously lives according to a fabric of ideas that has as its basis a picture of ourselves and of the world about us. Such a picture is of course the interpretation man has gradually built up over the centuries of the impact this world makes upon those organs of sensation that are his sole means of contact with it. It has not been static but has grown with all human experience. From time to time a great discovery may modify it profoundly. Nevertheless all men have developed a view of the natural world which is essentially the same in its general outlines and which is universally accepted as corresponding, at least approximately, to what this world is actually like. Natural science necessarily has its origin in this universal picture. It grows by devising new forms of experience that will illuminate and extend our inheritance.

The mere fact that it is practically impossible to talk about our integrated knowledge of the outer world except in visual terms shows how dependent we are on sight as our most highly developed sense, both as a guide to life in this world of nature and as our chief source of information about it. Vision is not, to be sure, the only source of useful sensory information nor is it any longer the dominant factor in human culture: we learn first of the three-dimensional character of our world through tactile rather than visual experience and we require sound in order to express the vital human values that lie in language and music. Nevertheless modern science remains overwhelmingly the fruit of vision. It began toward the end of the Middle Ages as a sudden disquiet with aspects of the picture of the world that had been current for centuries. Much of its initial impetus came from the extension in vision made possible by the telescope and microscope. It has assumed its present importance partly because of the better picture it gives of the significance of man in nature but very largely because of the discovery that an increasing natural knowledge can become our principal source of material wealth and well-being.

A discussion of the factors that probably were influential in causing our forefathers to take so much greater an interest in the material world would be out of place here; but it is pertinent to point out that the natural science which has resulted is the product, first, of a steady increase in the delicacy and extent of our sensory perceptions and, second, of the deeper realization that everything that happens in the world of matter seems to proceed according to a system of inexorable law that becomes more recognizable as these perceptions are amplified. This enhancement of a sensory contact with nature was made possible through the introduction of the planned experiment, which, instead of depending only on things that occur spontaneously, made them happen in such a way as to answer significant questions about the ways of nature. To implement this attitude and improve his sensory contacts with his world, seventeenth-century man began inventing instruments. Since then experimental science has grown at an accelerating pace through the development and exploitation of more and more of these instruments which have themselves been of a steadily increasing complexity. They have contributed in three different ways to this growth: some have been more delicate than our unaided senses in perceiving what goes on, some have given quantitative measures of what is happening that are beyond the capacity of our essentially qualitative perceptions, and some have recorded happenings that are beyond the range of sensitivity of the sense organs with which nature has endowed us.

Inevitably those instruments involving vision have had a dominant place corresponding to the pictorial character of the synthesis we instinctively make of sensory experience. In its most primitive form the optical microscope was of course one of the first of these. Its overwhelming importance lay in its demonstration that there actually exists a world of the very small whose contents need not remain merely a subject for speculation but can be observed and interpreted with the same directness as objects seen by the unaided eye. Like most early instruments the microscope, in providing us with what is effectively an eye of very short focal length, is an example of that first stage of instrumentation which seeks to extend the sensitivity of our senses.

Other types of instrument are more recent. Thus the last half century has seen the invention of a number of substitutes for our senses as agents of direct contact with the outer world. These synthetic sense organs have been successful in providing still more quantitative information, in supplying still more sensitive detectors of the impulses to which our sense organs are attuned, and in extending our awareness of nature to radiant impact of a kind that leaves them completely unaffected. Along these lines there have been developed in the laboratory receptors for all sorts of electromagnetic radiations in addition to the visible light that affects the eye—for the ultraviolet and the infrared, for X rays and the long waves of radio. These re-

3

ceptors are as diverse as the photographic emulsion, photoelectric surfaces, the Geiger and other counting devices and the antennae of radar. All are supplements to vision in its broadest sense. We are not, of course, limited to using them for the perception of radiations as these occur in nature. Invisible radiations can be generated in the laboratory even though they may never have been observed in nature; and it is largely through the study of the interaction of these man-made radiations with matter that the research of the last hundred years has taught so much that is new and unexpected about the fundamental nature of matter itself.

Extensions of vision have the especial value that arises from the directness with which their information can be interpreted. The world invisible radiations reveal is an enlargement of the world our eyes actually see and not a fundamentally different one; and we can interpret what they show in long-familiar ways without the possibilities of error that are always present with those often more elegant forms of experimentation where the observation is several intellectual steps removed from the explanatory picture to which it points. Electron microscopy offers numerous examples of this. Thus, as will later be shown, it can reveal directly the distribution of the molecules that make up the crystals of many biological and organic substances. We can also deduce this molecular arrangement from a detailed consideration and analysis of the many hundreds or thousands of X-ray diffractions which one of these crystals will produce. The result is the same, but seeing how the molecules are distributed carries with it an aesthetic pleasure and immediate assurance of correctness that counterbalances the perhaps richer intellectual satisfaction which a successful X-ray analysis provides.

Synthetic sense organs and the instruments that employ them deal with radiations which, like light, are part of the electromagnetic spectrum. The electron microscope is fundamentally different because it is a device, perhaps the first, for directly perceiving nature with radiation that is not a part of this spectrum. The vision it gives is the more important since in this sense it is different in kind, and not merely in range of sensitivity, from that given by light and its electromagnetic extensions. It was completely unforeseen, nor could the possibility of it have been imagined, till after totally unrelated work had established the equally unanticipated wave properties of electrons.

Chapter 2 | ELECTRON OPTICS

IF WE are to understand what electron microscopy is [1] and the unique and novel contributions that it can make to our knowledge of the fine structure of matter, it is first necessary to refer to those properties of electrons which permit us to employ them for microscopy and to see with them what otherwise could not be rendered visible.

The cathode rays which were much later found to be streams of electrons were discovered in the middle of the last century when physicists began to study the phenomena seen in evacuated glass vessels through which electrical discharges were passing. They were recognized as rays proceeding from the negative electrode by the glow they caused in such a fluorescent material as the mineral willemite (Fig. 1). It was early noted that the luminescence, and hence the cathode rays themselves, were easily deflected by a magnet held close to the tube, but their nature remained in doubt and a subject of vigorous debate for many years. In 1897 they were proved by the experiments of J. J. Thomson to consist of a stream of negative electricity made up of electrons which were unit charges of this negative electricity, each having $\frac{1}{1800}$ the mass of an atom of hydrogen. A part of this demonstration involved showing that, provided the vacuum was good enough, the cathode rays could be deflected by an electrical as well as by a magnetic field. This ready deflectibility of electrons is what makes it possible to construct lenses that will manipulate and focus them in much the way light is focused by lenses of glass. The possibility of making electron lenses was not, however, realized for another thirty years until theoretical work on how to focus them was published in 1927. In this same year the discovery that electrons are diffracted as are X rays in passing through a crystal demonstrated that, though particles, they also behave as if they have extremely short wave lengths. Soon thereafter the attempt was begun in Germany to build a microscope taking advantage of these two

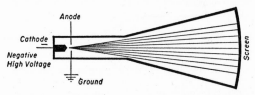

Fig. 1. A section through a simple cathode ray tube showing the arrangement of its essential parts. Electrons from the cathode are accelerated between it and the grounded anode and, passing through the hole in the anode plate, travel down the evacuated tube in straight paths. The fluorescent coating of the screen is now usually a metallic sulfide rather than the mineral willemite. The cathode, which originally was a piece of aluminum, is now almost always a length of tungsten wire heated to incandescence.

developments, but nearly ten years were required before one could be produced that was as good as the optical microscope. Thereafter development was rapid, and we now have had for nearly twenty years instruments of steadily increasing quality which will reveal hitherto unseen details of the fine structure of matter.

Lenses can be built using either electrical or magnetic fields to concentrate the electrons. Of these the electrostatic lens is in some respects the simpler. It makes use of the fact that the deflection of electrons takes place as they pass through a region of abruptly changing electrical potential. To concentrate and

7

thus focus them as they pass down a cathode ray tube such as that of Figure 1, the field must be circular in cross section. This result could be most easily obtained by inserting end to end in the path of the beam a pair of short metallic tubes (Fig. 2) charged to different potentials. The beam would then be bent

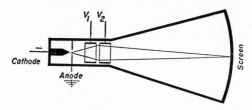

Fig. 2. An electrostatic focusing of the electrons in a tube such as that of Figure 1 can be obtained by inserting a pair of adjacent metal cylinders charged to two different voltages, V_1 and V_2.

everywhere toward the axis in the field between the tubes. In practice an electrostatic lens usually consists not of a pair of tubes but of three plates bored axially and arranged so that the insulated central plate is at a high potential with respect to the outer two which are electrically grounded (Fig. 3). The focal length of such a lens, and therefore its magnification, depend on the nearness of the plates, on their bore, and on the difference of potential between them. When the latter is of the order of some tens of thousands of volts the focal length can be as short as one to two millimeters, a value comparable with that of the objective lens in an optical microscope.

The simplest magnetic lens is a ring-shaped permanent magnet which, by reason of the changing fields at its two ends, will concentrate a beam of electrons passing along its axis. The simplest electromagnetic electron lens is a helical winding of wire (a solenoid) through which a direct current is flowing. When electrons are passed along the axis of such an electromagnet they will take helical paths through the coil but will be bent toward the axis at either end in the region of changing magnetic field. This change in field strength cannot be very abrupt around the ends of such an open coil which would serve only as a very weak lens of long focal length. The magnetic field can, however, be concentrated and the focal length shortened by enclosing the

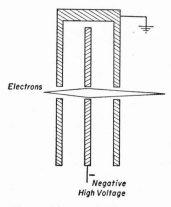

Fig. 3. The usual electrostatic lens has three components—a central plate maintained at a high negative potential with respect to the two on either side of it. The electrons pass through holes bored axially in these plates. In practice these elements are not simple plates but are shaped to prevent electrical discharges (corona) between them.

coil in iron except for a narrow internal band (Fig. 4) of copper or other nonmagnetic material.

The operation of such an electromagnetic lens is easily demonstrated by placing it, as in Figure 5, about the throat of a cathode ray tube such as was outlined in Figure 1. With increase of current through the coil the beam of electrons will become more constricted, as can be judged by the luminescence they produce in the fluorescent coating on the end of the tube. At

9

a certain current which depends on the number of turns of wire in the coil and on the voltage applied to the tube (that is, on

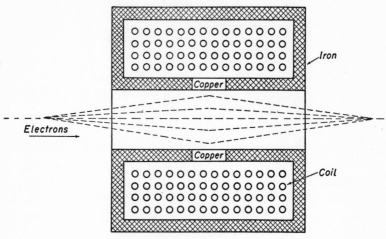

Fig. 4. A cross section through a simple electromagnetic electron lens. Electrons passing down the central tube are bent toward the axis as they pass through the magnetic field spreading from the non-magnetic copper break in the enveloping iron.

the electron velocity) the beam can be focused on the coating (Fig. 5). With a still greater current through the coil the circle of luminescence will again enlarge because the focal spot has moved up into the body of the tube (Fig. 6). This illustrates a difference between optical and electron lenses which is important to their use; because they have fixed focal lengths determined by their shapes, optical lenses are focused by moving them with respect to their objects; with electron lenses, on the contrary, this distance is usually fixed, and focusing is achieved by changes of applied current or potential.

The still more concentrated field needed to produce a lens of very short focus can be obtained by inserting a pole piece

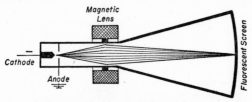

Fig. 5. The electron beam will be made to converge when an electromagnetic lens, such as that shown in Figure 4, is placed about the cathode ray tube of Figure 1.

within such an electromagnet (Fig. 7). It consists of two pieces of soft iron which may be separated by a "spacer" of brass but in any case are bored axially with a hole through which the electrons travel. There is no difficulty in making the field in the narrow gap between the two iron pieces so great that the lens will have a focal length of one to two millimeters.

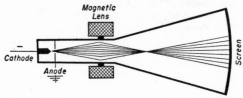

Fig. 6. With more current through the electromagnetic lens of Figure 5, its focal length becomes shorter.

The electron microscope is but one of a number of new electron optical instruments that can be constructed with these electron lenses. The first scientific instrument to use them to produce a focused beam of electrons was in fact the cathode ray oscilloscope. If a cathode ray tube such as that of Figure 5 contains also a pair of electrodes such as those at B of Figure 8, a voltage applied across the pair of plates will deflect the electron beam and thus move the focused spot in one direction. By inserting two pairs of plates at right angles to one another the focused beam can be made to move to any point of the phos-

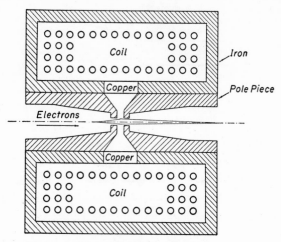

Fig. 7. A cross section, like that of Figure 4, through an electromagnetic lens equipped with a pole piece. A much more intense field now exists in the narrow gap between the two faces of the pole piece, and the greater bending of the electron paths that takes place here results in a lens of far shorter focal length.

phorescing screen. The cathode ray oscilloscope is such a tube. It is used routinely to analyze a periodically varying electrical potential by applying it to one set of plates while a standard alternating potential applied to the other pair provides a time scale. By a relatively simple modification this tube has become the television tube with which we have all grown so familiar. In it the focused spot moves very rapidly back and forth, not over the same line, but regularly over the entire surface of the phosphorescent screen; a picture is formed by making the intensity of the electron beam vary from moment to moment according to a pattern determined by an image at the scene being televised.

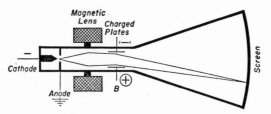

Fig. 8. When a pair of metallic plates is introduced into the tube of Figure 5 the position of a beam focused on the fluorescent screen can be displaced by an amount that depends on the voltage across the plates.

These are two examples of the type of electron optical instrument that makes use of a permanently focused beam of electrons. At a later point it will be indicated how such a "probe" is frequently useful in adding to the information an electron microscope can supply. This probe will usually be small and will be produced by lenses so placed as to give a reduced image of the electron source. The other general type of electron optical instrument with which we are concerned uses electron lenses to produce enlarged images which can then be studied for the information they contain either about the electron source itself or, as in the transmission electron microscope, about objects placed in the path of the electrons.

A most important attribute of electron lenses is that they follow the rules of geometrical optics in focusing electrons. This means that in computing the relation between focal lengths and component magnifications, or in deciding how they should be combined to produce an image of a desired magnification, we can use the same formulas that apply to glass lenses focusing light. These are the familiar (Fig. 9)

$$\frac{1}{F_1} + \frac{1}{F_2} = \frac{1}{f}$$

and the magnification $M = F_2/F_1$. Some of the instruments that are built by combining electron lenses imitate optical instruments in the kind of information they can provide; others,

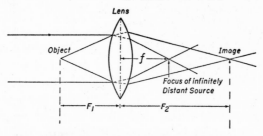

Fig. 9. A drawing to illustrate the usual relation between focal length and object-image distance of optical and electron lenses.

making use of the unique properties of electrons, can give information unlike that supplied by optical instruments. It is to the various applications of this developing electron optics in the broad field of microscopy that the present account is addressed.

Chapter 3 | ELECTRON MICROSCOPES

IN ALL our attempts to understand matter two of the fundamental questions we invariably ask are concerned with first, its form and secondly, its composition. Microscopy is in the main preoccupied with the first of these, though in late years it has come to contribute useful data about chemical composition, originally with the help of ultraviolet radiation and more recently through the use of specific stains. Electron optical instruments also can be constructed which will yield both of these types of information.

The idea of employing electrons for microscopy arose both from the realization that the optical microscope had already attained the theoretical limit of what it could do in seeing the very small and because the extreme shortness of the waves associated with electrons offered a possible escape from the impasse thus created.

Before the end of the last century the theory of the optical microscope had been developed to demonstrate the inflexible relation that exists between the wave length of light and the smallness of the object that can be imaged by any optical system. It showed that such a small object will have a diameter approximately half the wave length being employed. Thus, we can see smaller things in a microscope with blue than with the longer red light; and the smallest thing we can hope to see or photograph, using visible light, will have a diameter of about half the wave length of violet light, that is about

15

$$\frac{4000 \text{ A}}{2} = 2000 \times 10^{-8} \text{ cm} = 0.0002 \text{ mm} =$$

$$0.2 \times 10^{-3} \text{ mm} = 0.2 \text{ micron}.$$

Before 1900 the better microscopes were able to reveal objects of this size.

The lower limit to what can be imaged by an optical system is expressed by its resolving power, which is defined in terms of the ability to see as separate two objects that are very close together. When toward the end of the last century it was realized that the limit in resolving power of the microscope using visible light was being reached, greater resolution was sought through the use of ultraviolet light. This required lenses of some material other than the glass which is not transparent to the ultraviolet. Crystalline quartz lenses were designed and built to employ light of about 2700 A, or nearly half the wave length of blue light. The microscope that used them therefore was capable under ideal conditions of almost twice the resolution of the optical microscope. It could form images of small objects approaching 0.1 micron in diameter. Quartz is opaque at much shorter wave lengths but it would have been possible to make lenses of the somewhat more transparent mineral fluorite. The technical difficulties of operating a microscope would have increased rapidly at wave lengths shorter than about 2200 A; because of the opacity of nearly all matter below about 1500 A, no material exists for making the equivalent of an optical microscope's lenses. Thus there is no hope of increased resolution through further extension of the optical microscope. It is true that nowadays we are beginning to make and to work with so-called X-ray microscopes, but they are either optically crude devices using total reflection or lensless, pinhole projectors. There is no immediate prospect that either will be able to delineate particles appreciably smaller than those to be seen with ordinary light.

Their possible contributions, though valuable, lie in quite other directions (p. 66 ff.).

In view of these limitations to seeing the very small through the use of visible light and the rest of the electromagnetic spectrum, it was inevitable that realization of the exceedingly short wave lengths of electrons would give microscopic research quite a new direction. When electrons are accelerated through 50,000 volts, which happens to be a convenient voltage to employ, they have a wave length that is only about $\frac{1}{100,000}$ that of light; in other words, their wave length is only about 0.05 A. The theoretical limit to their resolving power, about half this value, is thus far less than the diameter of an atom. If there should ever be any practical point to be gained thereby, this limit could be still further reduced by using higher voltages; or radiation consisting of more massive particles, like the protons which are charged hydrogen atoms, with their still shorter wave lengths, could replace the electrons. Very evidently what we can see is no longer limited by the resolving power of the radiations at our disposal. It is instead determined by our current ability to make an instrument that will utilize as much as possible of this potential resolution.

It is worth emphasizing this sequence of events leading up to the invention of the electron microscope because it is so clearly an example of how what we learn about nature through the experiments we elect to make is imprisoned within the framework of the ideas we currently hold. There could have been an electron microscope fifty or sixty years ago; one was actually built, not when a series of technical advances finally made it possible, but when the discovery of electron diffraction, in no way connected with microscopy, so changed our fundamental outlook that an instrument using electrons seemed to offer a way to escape from the impasse that then blocked further development.

The preceding partly historical considerations make it easier to understand what electron microscopes are and why they are playing so important and irreplaceable a role in the study of the fine structure of matter. Microscopes are by definition instru-ments which will produce an enlarged image of an object. They are of a wide variety of types. The simplest we can imagine has no lenses and makes use of a minute source of illumination. Thus if, as in Figure 10, an object at B is illuminated by light,

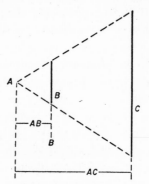

Fig. 10. A drawing to show the relation in a shadow-microscope be-tween magnification and position of the object with respect to the source and the image plane.

or electrons, coming from a point source at A, there will be formed at any plane C an enlarged shadow-image of B. The greater the distance AC compared to AB, the larger the image at C—in other words, the higher the magnification. The amount of detail which appears in this image will depend on the relative opacity of different parts of the object B, and also on the size of the source A. With a bigger A the resolution will be poorer and the detail of the image will become fuzzier. It is not hard to calculate the relation between the two, and it turns out that the size of the smallest detail of B to be seen in C is about equal to the size of A. Shadow-microscopes built on this very simple principle are now being developed using X rays as source of illumination [2], and similar electron shadow-microscopes were made and tested in the early days of electron microscopy. They were of little practical value for the imaging of objects much below the limit of visibility in the optical microscope because of the technical difficulties of producing electron sources small enough for this purpose. Nevertheless, as will be shown later (Chapter 8), types of microscope having very small sources can be made that will give information unattainable in any other way about both the microstructure and the chemical composition of certain objects.

Most electron microscopes are like optical microscopes in using lenses to produce enlarged images of their objects; indeed that type which is most generally useful and is meant by the term electron microscope imitates in its design the familiar compound optical microscope. The essentials of such a microscope are an objective lens of short focal length and high component magnification, and a weaker projector (or eyepiece) lens to enlarge further the image formed by the objective. It must have an illuminating system which consists of a source (of light or electrons) and a condensing lens to collect and direct this illumination upon an object placed between this lens and the objective. The close analogy between the two microscopes will be clear from Figure 11. Since electrons can travel appreciable distances only in a vacuum, these several components of the electron microscope, together with a screen covered with fluorescent material for viewing the image that is formed and a holder for the photographic plate to record it, must be enclosed in a vacuum-tight system (the "column"). A complete electron microscope is thus a rather complicated device, partly because of this need to operate in vacuo and partly because the column must be supplemented by an adequate pumping system to maintain the high vacuum and by carefully stabilized electrical supplies of current for the lenses and of high voltage to accelerate

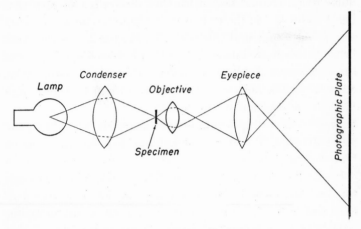

Fig. 11. A comparative drawing showing the distribution of the essential lens components of an optical microscope (above) and a simple transmission electromagnetic electron microscope (below).

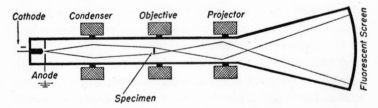

the electrons. Other complicating features must be added to those instruments which aim for the highest resolution. They require a wider range of magnifications, which is achieved by adding a so-called intermediate lens between objective and projector and, in some instruments, by having a series of projectors. Work at high resolution likewise requires more precise control and limitation of the beam illuminating the specimen;

in the best microscopes this is accomplished by adding a second condensing lens. With all these complications an electron microscope becomes an expensive affair, the simplest costing in the neighborhood of $10,000 and the most complex five times this amount [3]. An indication of the rapid expansion now occurring in research in the natural sciences as well as of the broad range of the possible applications for electron microscopes can be gained from the fact that about fifteen hundred of these instruments have been manufactured over the last ten years with a steadily increasing demand for more.

Electron microscopes have been built with either electrostatic or electromagnetic lenses. Each kind has its advantages and its disadvantages, but the microscopes capable of the highest resolution are electromagnetic. In its simplest form such a microscope has the components indicated in Figure 11. As is the case with radio and most other electron tubes, a tungsten wire heated to incandescence is the electron source. Originating in the tip of this wire in the gun, the electrons are accelerated by a difference of potential of 50–100 kilovolts between it and the anode, and are aligned for illuminating the specimen by the condenser lens. An intermediate image of the specimen is formed by the short-focus objective, and a portion of this image is further enlarged by passage through the projector to produce the final image. This can be seen by the luminescence it causes in the phosphorescent screen, and photographed on a similarly placed plate or film. Additional lenses that increase the versatility of most modern instruments alter in detail but not in principle this explanation of the microscope in its simple form.

Advantage is taken of the variable focal length of electron lenses to keep the specimen–objective lens distance constant. In operation the final magnification is determined by the chosen projector current, and the image is focused by changing the current through the objective lens. Magnification is increased by

21

shortening the focal length of the projector and making the compensatory shift in the focal length of the objective requisite for a sharp image.

An electron microscope with electrostatic lenses is the same basic combination of components. Its electrical supplies are, however, simpler because its lenses can be actuated by the same high voltage that is used to accelerate its electrons (Fig. 12). This is perhaps its chief advantage: it makes possible moderately

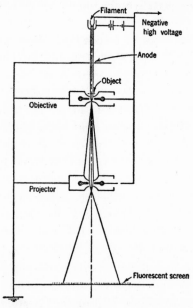

Fig. 12. A drawing to show the electrical interconnections of the lenses and high-voltage supply in an electrostatic electron microscope. In this simple design the condenser has been omitted.

satisfactory performance with a power supply that is much less constant than is required for a microscope having magnetic lenses. The reason for this will be apparent from the figure. If the voltage declines, for instance, then the electrons are slower and hence more easily deflected; but at the same time the lenses become weaker. In this way the two effects tend to balance one another out and maintain a constant focus. If it were more difficult than it now is to make power supplies having the constancy required by the best electromagnetic microscopes, this property of the electrostatic microscope would have been of great value. For reasons to be given later, electrostatic lenses are optically inferior to those of the magnetic type and cannot therefore be employed to obtain the highest resolution. Perhaps when the further evolution of electron microscopy has created more applications which can be satisfactorily made with instruments that are moderate in performance and far cheaper to build, electrostatic microscopes will again be found useful.

The electron microscopist must always bear in mind that his electromagnetic instrument contains several features that act or may act as electrostatic lenses. Thus both the cap that surrounds the tungsten filament and the anode have circular openings through which the electrons pass. They are at potentials different from one another and from the tungsten source, and consequently each has some lens action on the electron beam. Electrostatic lenses of an objectionable character are always being created by the accumulation of "dirt" and nonconducting layers upon all orifices that are struck by electrons. Care must constantly be taken to eliminate through cleaning the charges thus being built up on apertures and the distortions in the image that result from their acting in this way as very faulty lenses.

Chapter 4 | ELECTRON IMAGES

WHAT we can see with electrons is of course determined by the interactions between them and the object under study. The physical processes are different from those that take place when light is used, and are perhaps most easily understood by comparing what occurs when an object is viewed in an electron and in an optical microscope. Whenever we see with our unaided eyes something which is not, like a lamp or a flame, itself emitting light, it is because it is reflecting, absorbing, or sometimes refracting some of the light with which it is being illuminated. In a metallurgical microscope a specimen of metal is seen by the light it reflects; a biologist looking at tissue in the ordinary optical microscope distinguishes its components because the dyes with which they have been stained have rendered these details opaque to certain wave lengths of light. Scattering, rather than either absorption or reflection, is the physical process responsible for the formation of a good electron microscopic image. Electrons are indeed absorbed by matter, but their complete absorption is the end result of a stepwise loss of energy; and any sample thick enough to bring it about is far too thick for satisfactory transmission microscopy. Scattering is the change in direction that occurs whenever electrons pass near an atom. It is of two sorts. It may take place without loss of velocity; or, through coming into more intimate contact with an atom, an electron may lose some of its energy. The first process is designated as coherent because interference can still take place between the wave systems associated with electrons thus scattered.

If the specimen is crystalline, diffraction phenomena analogous to those obtained with X rays may result. These must always be taken into account when interpreting what is seen; as will be shown later, often they are the basis for valuable information about chemical composition. The electrons that lose energy are said to be incoherently scattered; they are no longer able to produce crystalline diffraction. It is important to discriminate between these two scattering processes not only for their different roles in diffraction but because they do not make the same contribution to the electron microscopic image.

Most of the electrons that provide the luminous image seen on the fluorescent screen of an electron microscope have not come close enough to atoms in the object to have been scattered or otherwise influenced. Details within the object are visible against this background of unaffected electrons because many of the electrons that have been scattered have failed to reach their expected places in the image. Some of these will be deflected widely enough to be stopped by apertures; those incoherently scattered electrons which have been slowed down but deflected through smaller angles will be unduly bent in passing through the lenses and hence will reach the image in the wrong places. The visible detail has scattered enough electrons so that a perceptible "hole" is created in the image, in the same sense that absorption of light in an optical microscope leaves a corresponding deficit in the optical image. The measure of this deficit is of course the contrast that is produced. Scattering is due to atoms acting individually and not in molecular or other groups. A heavy atom scatters many more of the electrons that pass near it than does one of low atomic number and hence its presence in a structural detail or macromolecule enhances greatly the contrast that makes it recognizable.

This contrast is a factor as important as resolution for determining how small an object the electron microscope can reveal. Unfortunately present knowledge of the scattering processes is not sufficiently quantitative to permit computation of this minimum size of visible detail, but from the best estimates now possible it would appear that there can be enough scattering from a single atom to render one heavy but not one light atom perceptible. If this is true, light atoms must always be seen in clusters, that is to say as molecules, no matter how good our electron microscopes become.

Such a visualization of individual heavy atoms also requires a microscope having a resolving power of atomic dimensions. This has not been achieved and for reasons about to be discussed may not be reached in the near future; nevertheless the resolutions of 5–10 A, corresponding to three to five atomic diameters, that are now practical are not far from this goal.

The practical limit to attainable resolving power is now set by the perfection, considered as elements of an optical system, of the electron lenses we can make. They are subject to various defects which are analogous to those that exist in optical lenses. They cannot, however, be corrected by the same devices, with the result that the electron microscope is today a highly imperfect optical system. To a large degree its further development depends on the discovery of ways to minimize these lens defects. Experience with such uncorrected optical systems has taught that to get useful results from them they must be very severely apertured. Such an optical system of greatly reduced numerical aperture can provide a sharp image but at the expense of a corresponding reduction in limiting resolving power. The present-day electron microscope is such a heavily apertured system, which nevertheless is capable of extraordinarily high resolution, thanks to the extreme shortness of the electron waves it employs.

Though the defects that are found in electron lenses have physical causes entirely different from those that damage the quality of images produced by lenses of glass, the fact that the same laws of geometrical optics apply to both makes it convenient to use for electron lenses the designations that are already familiar. Some of the defects which must be considered by the designer of an optical system are unimportant to the electron microscopist, but there are four that are of great importance. They determine the performance of existing instruments and must be understood if we are to appreciate both the possibilities for and the limitations to future improvement. These lens defects express themselves (a) as a spherical aberration, (b) as the equivalent of a chromatic aberration which has its origin in inequalities in the electron velocities, (c) as an astigmatism that arises from faults of composition and construction in the pole pieces, and (d) as various image distortions that arise in the projector lens.

The defect which is at present the most important factor in limiting the attainable resolving power is spherical aberration. With electron lenses as with those for light it expresses the fact that rays which pass through the lens along its axis and at some distance from this axis are not brought to focus at exactly the same distance from the lens. The field of the lens, whether electrostatic or electromagnetic, is not uniform and is minimal at the axis; as a consequence nonaxial electrons are more strongly deflected and always come to focus ahead of those that are axial. Glass lenses are corrected for spherical aberration by grinding them to such a shape that axial and nonaxial beams have a common focus. There is, however, as yet no practical way of equalizing the field strength across an electron lens to accomplish a similar result. The only way to reduce this aberration is by keeping the opening of the lens small, but with too much aperturing diffraction effects would become damaging. It has been calculated that for a magnetic lens the best compromise between these limitations will permit a maximum attainable

27

resolution in the neighborhood of 4 A, which corresponds to a particle two or three atoms across. The corresponding calculated compromise for an electrostatic lens leads to a spherical aberration constant several times that for a magnetic lens. This is an important reason why electrostatic lenses are not now employed in microscopes of high resolving power.

In optical instruments chromatic aberrations arise because light of different wave lengths is differently bent in passing through a glass lens. Electrons traveling with different velocities and therefore having different wave lengths are responsible for the "chromatic" aberrations of electron optics. In an electron microscope these aberrations can have two origins. They will, for one thing, be produced by any variations that occur in the accelerating high voltage. Electrons thus caused to move at different velocities will be focused at different points along the axis and produce a decided fuzzing of the image. Such fluctuations in the high voltage need not occur in a good present-day electron microscope where the accelerating voltage can be maintained constant to one volt in 50,000. Greater constancy would not help since the electrons in leaving the emitting hot wire have small velocities of their own corresponding to a volt or two. Fortunately a greater uniformity is not required.

The chromatic effects that must be worried about are due to the electrons incoherently, i.e., inelastically, scattered in the sample. These cannot be so easily eliminated. An electron thus scattered loses on an average the energy corresponding to a deceleration through 15 volts; and this scattering may happen more than once in specimens of an appreciable thickness. Small apertures below the specimen will exclude many of these slower moving electrons from the final image and thus contribute usefully to its contrast; but the rest will be focused ahead of the other electrons and deteriorate the image by making it diffuse. Since the amount of this chromatic fuzzing depends on the total number of inelastically scattered electrons, it increases with both the thickness of the object and the area being illuminated. Experience shows that it gives rise to a serious loss of sharpness in the image when the object, considered as a continuous film, is more than about 200 A thick. Examination at the highest resolutions requires a far thinner specimen than this, supported on the thinnest possible substrate.

Unlike spherical and chromatic aberrations, astigmatism is an important defect which can now be fully eliminated through correction. It is present in an electron optical system when a point appears as a line in front of the plane of the image and as another line at right angles to the first behind the plane; in the plane itself the two lines merge to yield a "circle of confusion" which is larger the greater the astigmatism. Electron astigmatism has an origin entirely different from that encountered in optical systems; it is caused by mechanical faults or magnetic inhomogeneities leading to an asymmetry in the field of the pole piece. Unless it is too great it can be corrected by introducing a weak additional field to compensate for this asymmetry. In practice this has been done by adding a "stigmator" that surrounds the image-forming electron beam with soft iron magnetic elements or by a ring of opposed electrodes. Compensation is achieved by moving these magnets or applying small voltages across the pairs of electrodes.

The image in an electron microscope is most damaged by astigmatism in its objective lens. Consequently the objective lenses of microscopes designed for high resolution are equipped with a stigmator placed below the specimen either in the gap between the two halves of the objective pole piece or below the objective near its focal point. The adjustments of the stigmator to eliminate astigmatism are made while observing the image produced by a semitransparent test object which is usually either a minute hole in a plastic film or tiny particles of carbon deposited from burning camphor or a similar organic compound. Just as in the analogous optical situation, the edges of such an object will be surrounded on either side of focus by one or more Fresnel fringes. The symmetry with which these fringes disappear on the underfocused side and develop on the overfocused side as its focusing current is increased is a direct indication of the astigmatism in the objective lens. In practice correction is made by manipulating the stigmator till these fringes show no asymmetry as they develop; astigmatism will cease to interfere with work at the highest attainable resolution only when no asymmetry can be seen in an image viewed at a magnification of at least 100,000 times. All objective pole pieces must be corrected in this way if high resolutions are to be attained, since it would only be by chance that one could be made that showed no observable astigmatism; and even a microscope having such a pole piece would soon develop astigmatism because of the accumulation of particles and films of foreign matter on it or on the apertures introduced to provide contrast. This is accordingly an adjustment that cannot be made once and for all but must be carried out at frequent intervals. The astigmatism of projector lenses does not damage the image, nor does that of the condenser unless two condensers are employed to give a very small area of specimen illumination. Then one must be equipped with a stigmator to render circular the elongated spot that otherwise would be produced.

The fourth lens defect, distortion, that can bother the electron microscopist arises whenever the magnification is not uniform over the plane of the image. When this occurs it has its origin in the projector and is to be attributed to the spherical aberration inherent in this lens. It has in the past been a problem only when using the microscope at relatively low magnification. Now that we appreciate the need to work at these magnifications in order to relate what the electron microscope reveals to what has previously been learned with the optical microscope, changes in design have rendered distortion negligible. In the better microscopes it is no longer a problem.

In the day-by-day application of an electron microscope it is necessary to have an adequate measure of the resolution it is giving. This is rendered difficult by the absence of suitable standard samples. Particulate deposits of a heavy metal such as gold or platinum are most commonly used to estimate very high resolutions. These can be the particles in an exceedingly fine colloidal suspension or in a very light film evaporated on the thinnest possible supporting substrate. Such a film as seen under the requisite intense illumination will appear as an aggregate of minute granules nearly in contact; resolution is determined by measuring the minimum distance between clearly separated particles. The best separations thus seen are somewhere in the neighborhood of 6 A. This is very near indeed to the theoretical lower limit of 4 A set by damaging effects of the spherical aberration that cannot now be eliminated.

The smallest objects that can in practice be seen with the best microscopes are usually appreciably bigger than this. This limit in size depends very much on the type of specimen being studied and on the state of cleanliness that can be maintained within the microscope for this type of specimen. One factor, already mentioned, which is of great importance is the slight contrast produced by scattering in very thin specimens unless heavy atoms are present. Another is the particularly serious problem of preventing contaminating deposits from obscuring small detail. This contamination is of two sorts. For one thing nearly all preparations will be covered over with layers at least a few molecules thick of impurities derived from the reagents used in making them. The loss in visibility this entails becomes more serious the smaller the detail and the lighter its atoms. The other contamination is the deposit that so rapidly forms on the specimen in all present-day electron microscopes. Under the intense electron bombardment involved in work at high magnifications, these deposits grow at rates often in excess of 60 A per minute of exposure of the sample. Especially with biological specimens they often obliterate before photographs can be made the fine detail one hopes to reveal. As a consequence most work at resolutions higher than 20–25 A becomes very difficult, and until adequate methods have been developed to reduce the rate of accumulation of this contamination the meaningful work that can be done in the region between 10 A and 20 A is strictly limited. Such methods are possible, although those that immediately suggest themselves are inelegant and will add to the complexity of our experimental procedures.

The development of the electron microscope has now brought us so near to seeing individual atoms that it is interesting to inquire what chance there is of bridging the small gap that remains. As we have seen, the uncorrected spherical aberration of electron lenses makes it improbable that the required small improvement in resolving power, from about 6 A to about 2 A, can be made in the near future. This gives added importance to other, related ways of extending vision.

One of these that theoretically might be advantageous would employ charged atomic particles with their still shorter wave lengths in place of electrons as illumination in a microscope. Such ion microscopes have been built. The simplest of course uses protons [4]. The wave length associated with these positively charged hydrogen atoms is only $\sqrt{m_e/m_H}$ (m_e and m_H are

masses of the electron and hydrogen atom) $= \sqrt{1/1836} = \dfrac{1}{43}$

that of electrons accelerated through the same potential difference. The theoretically attainable limit of resolution for protons is correspondingly smaller than the limit for electrons. There are, however, at least two serious difficulties encountered in making a proton microscope which will have a resolution even as high as that obtained with electrons. One of these centers around the problem of producing a satisfactory illuminating beam of protons of sufficiently uniform velocity. The other, which somewhat mitigates the first, arises from the need to employ electrostatic lenses with their higher spherical aberration. An electromagnetic proton microscope is scarcely feasible because for a magnetic lens of given strength the focal length increases, and the magnification therefore decreases, with the mass of the particle. Electrostatic lenses, however, deflect the heavy protons as effectively as the light electrons. A proton microscope was first constructed several years ago. Its resolution has not yet been comparable with that of the electron microscope but is still being improved. At first it was feared that a beam of high-speed protons would so thoroughly damage the fine structure of matter in its path that few objects could profitably be examined. Preliminary work indicates, however, so much scattering of protons even by light elements that this fear seems to have been groundless. In fact the greater attainable contrast resulting from this scattering, rather than very high resolutions, may be the most attractive feature of the proton microscope.

Microscopes using charged atoms heavier than hydrogen are also possible, and lithium ion microscopes have been constructed [5]. The lithium ion, consisting of the lithium nucleus and its attendant K electrons, is enormously bigger than the hydrogen nucleus which is the proton. This large size would be expected to make lithium ions far more destructive to the organization of matter in their path, and this seems to be borne out by experience. Probably whatever advantages ion microscopes may have will be realized with protons.

Though the proton microscope that imitates the transmission electron microscope does not bring us nearer to seeing individual

33

atoms, their effects can apparently be observed with the so-called field emission microscope [6]. This is in principle a very simple device which, like the projection microscopes already discussed (p. 18), avoids the use of electron lenses. It consists merely of an exceedingly fine metallic point sealed at very high vacuum into a tube containing a second electrode and a fluorescent screen (Fig. 13). If the point is made cathode and a voltage of

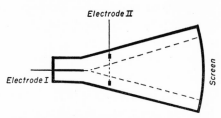

Fig. 13. The essential components of a point projection microscope. When acting as an electron microscope the point (electrode I) is negative; when functioning as a proton microscope it is positive with respect to electrode II.

some tens of thousands of volts is applied between the two electrodes, the field around the point is so intense that electrons are drawn from it and projected in paths at right angles to the surface from which they issue. They will thus produce an image of the point on the fluorescent screen at a magnification which is the ratio of the distance of the point from the screen divided by the radius of the point. By carefully etching the metallic point this radius can be made so small that millionfold magnifications are attained. The number of electrons emitted over such a point is strongly influenced by the orientations of the microcrystals of which it is composed and by films of any material adsorbed on it. The image seen on the screen mirrors this crystallinity and the adsorbed layers at resolutions comparable with those of the best electron microscopes. It has been shown that

34

after condensing a little phthalocyanin on the point, patterns having the known shape of its molecules appear on the screen. They probably should be considered as shadow-representations of these unusually stable and not particularly large organic molecules.

Still higher resolutions have recently been obtained by employing this arrangement as a proton instead of an electron microscope. This is done by reversing the polarity of the electrodes, operating the tube at a low pressure of hydrogen instead of at high vacuum, and maintaining the point at the very low temperature of liquid air. Under these conditions the hydrogen molecules that adsorb on the point are then projected from it as protons. Their adsorption varies with the different crystalline faces exposed on the point, and the pattern produced by the ejected protons that reach the screen seems to reproduce the known distribution of the metallic atoms over these faces. The patterns have shown what appear to be rows of atoms possessing the crystalline order of the metal as modified by the defects in atomic arrangement that characterize real as contrasted with ideal crystals.

The applications of field emission microscopes are severely limited by vacuum requirements that are especially stringent when electrons are employed, as well as by the need to work with the few metals that can be made into exceedingly fine uncontaminated points. Nevertheless they offer not only an intriguing way to visualize atomic phenomena but a valuable technique for studying both crystalline perfection and many problems of adsorption.

Chapter 5 | SPECIMENS FOR ELECTRON MICROSCOPY

THE ELECTRON MICROSCOPE resembles all other radically new instruments not merely in contributing new data to old problems but in drawing attention to novel questions that apply specifically to the unexplored province of nature upon which it intrudes. The discovery and formulation of these new problems has undoubtedly been the most fascinating aspect of the developing electron microscopy. The investigations that have followed such formulation have required new methods of specimen preparation in order to take adequate account of the unique way electrons interact with matter. When we bear this in mind, it is easy to understand why the broadening application of electron microscopy has been so closely linked to improvements in specimen preparation and why this will continue to be so for a long time to come. In fact the properties of light and of electrons are so different that only very rarely can the same preparation be examined with profit in both the optical and the electron microscopes.

For electron microscopy an object must not suffer damage when placed in a vacuum and, as the previous discussion has shown, it must be unusually thin. Sometimes these conditions are cited as serious limitations to what the electron microscope can do, but as restrictions they are more apparent than real. Thus the vigorous Brownian motion that exists in living matter and other fluid systems must always and in some fashion be arrested if we are to see their minute detail. The desiccation to

which the electron microscopist as well as the optical cytologist
has recourse achieves this, perhaps as effectively as in any other
way that would now be practical. It is not impossible that we
may some day be able to view undried, deeply frozen specimens
in the electron microscope; but there are several reasons, including the poor contrast they would offer, why this would not now
be very instructive, even if it were possible. Similarly we would
need to look at very thin objects in the electron microscope even
if the properties of electrons did not require it. The improvement in resolution provides merely a confused mass of newly
visible fine detail unless it can be reduced through the examination of thinner preparations.

The types of preparation that have thus far been devised to
meet these conditions of dryness and thinness fall into three
general categories. The simplest is a suspension of particles of
microscopic or colloidal dimensions dried down or otherwise deposited on a very thin supporting film. This is the way to examine the components of a pigment, an ink or a dust, a fragment of muscle or tendon, a bacterium (Plate I) or the elementary infectious particles of a virus (Plates Xa and XIa). Replicas
of surfaces provide the second kind of specimen. Most of the
very extensive knowledge the electron microscope has already
given of the microstructure of solids has come from the study of
such replicas. Very many techniques have been proposed for
making these replicas but all yield as object for the microscope
an extremely thin film, one side of which reproduces the fine
detail of the surface in question. They can be employed to study
objects as diverse as an etched metal surface (Plate II), a piece
of tooth or bone, the surface of a fiber of wool or drawn plastic,
or the molecular arrangement in a protein crystal (Plate III).
As a third general type of preparation there are the thin slices
for direct examination that can now be cut from many solids.
These sections, which must usually be no more than a millionth

of an inch thick, are the best means of examining such materials as the tissues of living organisms (Plate IV), the internal structure of wood, and some still harder materials like rubber and the softer metals.

The importance of the electron microscope for science in general depends on the previously unseen fine detail it can reveal in specimens of the three types just mentioned. The range and richness of this detail below the limit of optical visibility are not easy to appreciate. The 10 A particles the electron microscope now reveals are as much smaller than the 2000 A particles at the lower limit of optical microscopic visibility as these are smaller than what the unaided eye can recognize. Inevitably, this hitherto unseen world contains all sorts of new information of both inorganic and biological importance. For inorganic substances, the electron microscope brings to light a type of structural organization that is an extension of what the optical microscope has already made evident. This further excursion into inorganic structure at the colloidal level is often helpful toward a better understanding of physical properties. Nevertheless, it is probable that the chief contribution of electron microscopy and its related techniques to the deeper understanding of inanimate matter will lie less in their additions to knowledge of structure than in the new methods they make possible for the chemical analysis of microquantities and selected micro areas of a solid. The electron microscope has a very different significance for biology because many of the chemical substances that constitute living matter have molecules big enough to be seen with it. The possibility of perceiving molecules has never before been seriously considered; it suggests a kind of visual physics and chemistry whose scope will become clear only after years of thought and imaginative experimentation. It is immediately obvious, however, that this molecular visualization gives a direct way to find out how living matter is organized on the macromolecular level and to observe the interplay of some of its molecules as they participate in reactions essential to the maintenance of life. There are limitless possibilities in so direct an approach to questions that the very existence of life presents.

A few years ago it would have been natural, now that we have considered the nature of the electron microscope, its possibilities and its limitations, to proceed to an account of what it has revealed at least over the last few years. This is no longer feasible since several thousand papers have been published during the last ten years within the restricted field of this specialty alone [7]. Some deal with problems of electron optical theory and the design of instruments, others with explorations of the microscope's possibilities and its necessary techniques, but most have described applications to specific, often utilitarian ends. Rather than attempt a catalogue of these applications we will choose a few as typical illustrations of the techniques that have been devised for applying the electron microscope to the new kinds of questions it has raised.

Though an electron microscopic specimen of sorts can be obtained merely by spreading particles of colloidal dimensions over a plastic film, making good preparations of particulate material requires careful attention to a number of procedures, most of which are also employed when making replicas and thin sections. Of paramount importance are ways to produce very thin films and to augment the visibility of minute particles that do not consist of heavy atoms.

All electron microscopic preparations, no matter what their character, must be supported on coherent films strong enough to withstand the impact of the electron beam and yet as transparent as possible to this beam. Such a supporting substrate must, therefore, be composed of light atoms and be not more than about 200 A thick. These membranous films are far too delicate to be handled directly and in most laboratories they are

39

supported and manipulated on metallic grids having about 200 meshes to the inch. Formerly they were of a wire cloth but now they are usually electrodeposited grids. Such a grid, though more fragile than the wire cloth, has the great advantage of providing a flat surface for the film it supports. A preparation of a particle suspension is made by allowing the particles to settle upon such a membrane-covered metallic grid. They may be settled on it directly as with a dust, or deposited from a microdrop of a suspension placed on the film. If they are so small that Brownian motion would interfere with settling, as would be the case, for instance, with the molecules of a protein, they may be attached by drying down an exceedingly dilute microdrop of the solution.

The need for films of the requisite thinness and strength has led to much instructive work directed toward their preparation. The simplest to make and those initially employed are of a plastic such as collodion or formvar. Films of collodion can be made from a solution in amyl acetate. When two or three drops of this solution fall on the surface of water filling a dish about a foot in diameter, they immediately spread over the surface and as the amyl acetate evaporates leave a hardened film of the desired thinness. A more general method which does not require as solvent a surface-spreading agent like amyl acetate forms the film by covering a clean glass slide with a dilute solution of plastic and allowing this to evaporate. The film thus formed is then floated onto a water surface. In either case it can be picked up on the metallic grids from the water, and when dry these are ready to use. For many purposes membranes made in this simple fashion are thin and strong enough. But when the substrate must be the thinnest possible, as in working at the highest resolutions, or when it must be unusually inert to chemicals, vacuum-evaporated films are necessary. They are made by evaporating under a good vacuum a layer of the material chosen for substrate onto a smooth surface from which it can subsequently be removed. Sometimes evaporation has been on a liquid like glycerin which has so low a vapor pressure that it can be put into the vacuum, sometimes on a freshly cleaved face of a crystal like rock salt which could later be dissolved away to leave the free-floating film. For most purposes it is easier to form the evaporated layer on a film of collodion or formvar. The greater strength of this composite film simplifies subsequent steps in the specimen preparation, and the plastic can be dissolved away before examination in the microscope. Evaporated films of a light metal such as aluminum or beryllium have thus been made to serve as substrates, as have those of silica obtained by the evaporation of SiO_2 or of the so-called silicon monoxide. The silica films are very strong but when thin are especially hard to see and hence to handle. Some years ago coherent membranes of a carbonaceous material, probably a hydrocarbon, were obtained as a deposit when an electrical discharge was passed at reduced pressure through the vapor of an organic compound like benzene. These films made good substrates but they changed on exposure to electrons and they often contained large particles of carbon from the inhomogeneous decomposition of the vapor. Far more satisfactory films of carbon are produced by evaporating graphite in a good vacuum [8]. This is easily done by passing a moderate current (ca. 30 amperes) between pointed, thin rods of pure graphite held lightly in contact. Such films show little structure at the highest electron microscopic magnifications, are inert to most chemicals, and are very strong when thin. Deposited on a film of formvar or collodion which is subsequently removed after the combined film has been mounted on grids, they are finding increasing use as the routine substrates of electron microscopy.

It has been reported that coherent films prepared of some of these materials have been no more than 20 A, that is about 10 atoms, thick. A film of appreciable area and as thin as this would be extremely fragile and too difficult to manipulate, but films less than 100 A thick are very rugged. Such films, especially those of evaporated carbon, are beginning to find use outside the field of electron microscopy where very thin windows of unusual strength and transparency to radiation are required.

Fig. 14. A drawing to illustrate the experimental arrangement required for vacuum evaporation. Atoms evaporating *in vacuo* from a substance placed in the heated tungsten spiral proceed in straight lines and are deposited on whatever surfaces they strike. To make thin films the collecting surface is usually placed directly below the filament. For shadowing it is placed off to one side.

Vacuum evaporation is extensively employed not only to make such substrates but to lay down thin films to serve other purposes in electron microscopy. The so-called shadowing that creates the enhanced contrast required for adequate visualization of many small objects and details is applied in this way. It is carried out by evaporating an exceedingly thin film of heavy atoms, usually as metal, obliquely over an otherwise finished preparation (Fig. 14). Many metals of moderate and high atomic number have been and are being used for this purpose—palladium, nickel, chromium, germanium, platinum, and uranium—as well as such compounds as tungsten trioxide and lanthanum oxide which volatilize apparently without decomposition. In the earlier days gold and chromium were favored, but gold has so low a melting point that it becomes granular under electron bombardment, and chromium is like some of the other metals just listed in having a perceptible fine structure which may be due to an oxide film. A shadowing layer of suitable thickness will be but faintly visible in the electron microscope; this corresponds to a mean thickness of no more than two or three of the heaviest atoms. The deposit will be thicker than this on the sides of detail facing the oncoming atoms while regions in the lee will be so shielded that, receiving little or no deposit, they will seem to be in shadow. The heavy atoms thus laid down on a very minute particle will greatly increase the contrast with which it is seen. The shadows that are cast will indicate through their lengths the heights and through their distribution the general shapes of objects (Plates I, II, III). As a result detail in a shadowed electron microscopic preparation is seen under conditions which call to mind the objects in a landscape as lighted by the rising or setting sun. This technique of shadowing has been invaluable in rendering visible biological particles and macromolecules and in indicating the shapes of denser objects whose contrast does not require reinforcement. It can be applied as long as the granularity of the evaporated film is less than that of significant detail in the specimen. Under present-day conditions of microscopy the most satisfactory shadowing agents have a granularity of the order of 20–30 A; the reality of smaller detail seen in shadowed preparations must be subject to serious question.

43

Chapter 6 | PARTICULATE PREPARATIONS

COLLOIDAL material which is not too strongly hydrated can be satisfactorily examined in the electron microscope after it has been deposited on a membrane-covered grid and shadowed. If, however, the water content is high, as is the case with micro-organisms, blood cells, many virus particles, and the macromole-cules of many proteins, drying is usually accompanied by serious flattening. There are several ways to avoid this flattening and the shrinkage that often occurs at the same time. Theoretically it can be done by drying from the frozen state. This requires instantaneous freezing of the suspension upon the supporting membrane and its maintenance frozen in a vacuum until all the water shall have sublimed. If the suspension is pure and es-pecially if its particles are minute, only the few that happen to be in contact with the supporting substrate when freezing takes place can be expected to remain attached to it after the sub-limation; the number of remaining particles can, however, be increased if a trace of a small molecular protein like egg or serum albumin is added to the suspension before freezing. During drying this forms a delicate mesh which, while resting in contact with the membrane, will entrap many more particles without adding perceptibly to their size. When such a binder is added a suspension can be effectively sprayed upon membrane-covered grids held at the temperature of dry ice or liquid air to ensure immediate freezing. This is the best method of specimen preparation to follow when seeking accurate measurements of particle dimensions.

When it is more important to prevent flattening than shrinkage, suspensions of hydrated particles can be prepared without freeze-drying. Dehydration can, for instance, be achieved by replacing the initial aqueous suspending medium with an organic liquid of low surface tension which cannot flatten the particles when it evaporates.

A more elaborate technique for avoiding distortions due to the surface tension of suspending fluids is the so-called critical point method [9]. It employs as final suspending liquid for the dehydrated particles a liquefied gas which can be vaporized at a temperature above its critical point. In using this procedure a sample is passed as in the preceding method through dehydrating liquids to one that is anhydrous, and placed in a bomb which can then be charged with a liquefied gas miscible with this final liquid. After the contents have been raised to a temperature above the critical point of the gas discharge is effected without the sample's passing through a liquid-vapor boundary. Preparations made in this way have very successfully preserved the shapes of bacteria and red cells and the relation of particles of bacteriophage to the bacteria they are infecting.

Stereoscopic examination of such unflattened specimens is especially rewarding. Cameras for taking stereoscopic pictures with light have two lens systems which, separated from one another by the distance between our eyes, take two pictures of the same object. This could scarcely be done with an electron microscope, but a stereoscopic pair of electron micrographs can be made by tilting the object between photographs. This tilt places different parts of the specimen at different distances from the objective lens, but the depth of focus of the microscope is sufficient so that sharp pictures can be made of those portions near the axis of tilt. If the development of shadowing had not given such an easy and routine way of observing the shapes of electron microscopic details, stereoscopic photography would have been much more important than it now is. In spite of this it can provide useful information about thick specimens and about films, for the most part replicas, that are far from being flat.

The flattening that occurs when bacteria and other biological objects are dried in air from aqueous suspension rather than by one of these more elaborate procedures is not always a disadvantage inasmuch as, unflattened, all but the smallest microorganisms are so thick that their internal structure cannot be seen. Some bacterial details are therefore very advantageously examined in air-dried specimens; others which involve structures that are fragile or that might be displaced by deformation should be studied only in thin sections.

The electron microscope can be used to establish the number as well as the dimensions of the particles in a colloidal suspension. This is done by adding a known amount of the uniform particles of a standard substance, usually a polystyrene latex, to the suspension being studied and spraying the mixture as minute droplets onto a substrate. Counts of the relative numbers of the two kinds of particles per microdrop are the data needed.

One of the most interesting electron microscopic investigations made of particulate inorganic matter deals with dusts and smokes. It is important for us here as an example of the way in which an old problem is changed by new data from electron optical instruments. For years much of the study of atmospheric pollution has been based on what is seen under the optical microscope. The relatively small amount of work thus far done with the electron microscope has shown that most of the particles in some dusts are submicroscopic and that many of those optically visible are aggregates of smaller particles [10]. There is much significance to such particles as previously unappreciated components and to the different biological reactions they may be expected to evoke. Cells of the body, and particularly of the lungs, should react in totally different ways to the large particles seen in the optical microscope and to the newly visible particles far smaller than themselves. The fates of large and small particles taken up by an animal through breathing or ingestion must be entirely different.

The electron microscopic techniques required for studies of this sort are adequately developed: it is not hard to make preparations of dust-laden air by precipitation on a thin membrane and to see dust within animals that have breathed it. Very little electron microscopy of air-contamination has yet been published; most of this deals with the silicosis produced in man by the silica-laden air of mines and quarries. As is generally known, the continued breathing of quartz and of certain silicates leads to serious pulmonary disease which frequently culminates in a fatal tuberculosis. Other forms of silica and other silicates are less hazardous.

The electron microscope not only gives a more realistic picture of the size distribution of particles in dusts and other suspensions but permits the chemical identification of their crystalline components through the electron diffraction that can be made simultaneously. In the case of siliceous dusts, it offers a convenient way of ascertaining the presence of quartz or dangerous silicates and of identifying their particles. Such identification can, of course, be made within the tissue of an animal as well as in the dust the animal may have breathed.

Electron diffraction is analogous to the X-ray diffraction which has provided our present extensive knowledge of the atomic positions in crystalline substances. The positions of X-ray diffractions are determined by a very simple relation $n \lambda = 2d \sin \theta$ between the wave length λ, the distance d between equidistant parallel planes that can be passed in many directions through the atoms of a crystal and the angle θ which is half the angle through which the diffraction occurs (n, the "order of reflection," has integral values). Since the exact positions of the atoms in a crystal vary from compound to compound and since nearly all solids are crystalline, these diffractions offer a widely applicable means of identifying solids. Electron diffraction is similarly useful. The wave length of the electrons we use is, however, only about ⅓₀ that of X rays, and electron diffractions will therefore occur at correspondingly small values of sin θ. This makes it easy to obtain and observe them within the angular limitations of the electron microscope. Most simply the specimen is placed for diffraction just below the projector of Figure 15 instead of in its usual position, the projector is turned off,

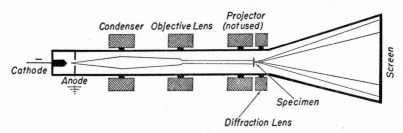

Fig. 15. A simple arrangement for obtaining electron diffraction from a crystalline sample using the electron microscope. A thick specimen in the position indicated here, but turned so that the nearly parallel electron beam grazes its surface, would give a "reflection" diffraction pattern on half of the screen.

and the condenser and objective illuminate the sample with a narrow beam of nearly parallel electrons. Many electron microscopes have an additional so-called diffraction lens below the projector to enlarge the diffraction pattern thus produced. If the sample is a mass of very tiny crystals this pattern will be a system of concentric rings (a powder diagram) whose relative intensities and diameters, each corresponding to one of the foregoing values of d, are characteristic of the substance producing them; if the crystals are larger the pattern from one or a few individuals will be an array of spots that is, however, less easy to interpret.

The diffraction patterns produced by the arrangement just described originate from a considerable area of a specimen and are characteristic of everything within this area. It is possible, however, by a relatively small change in the experimental arrangement to obtain diffraction from micro regions of a sample. In this fashion a positive chemical identification can often be made of individual particles which the electron microscope reveals in a mixture. Such an identification would tell, for instance, which of the particles we see in a dust were the disease-producing quartz and which some other relatively harmless mineral. This limited area diffraction, as it is called, is obtained by leaving the specimen in its usual place and having in the image plane below the objective lens two pairs of slits at right angles to one another which can be moved to exclude all but a chosen small area of the image. By this experimental arrangement one can carry out the usual electron microscopic examination of a particulate sample, and any chosen area down to about a micron (0.001 mm) on a side can then be isolated with the aid of the slits. The diffraction pattern from the crystal or crystals in the region thus seen can be observed by adjusting the lenses for diffraction.

This combination of electron microscopy and electron diffraction has a wide application to many inorganic particulate materials besides dusts. With pigments, for instance, it permits the investigation of the relation between covering power and particle size even when particles too small for optical visibility are present; and it makes possible the identification of components in powders that are mixtures of chemically different compounds or, as with titanium oxide, of different crystallographic modifications of the same compound. It is also being applied with growing success to the identification of the several microcrystal-line and poorly formed minerals that constitute clays, to the examination of catalysts, to following the production and aging of colloidal precipitates such as the hydrated oxides of iron or aluminum, and to the investigation of the mechanism of the photographic process.

Chapter 7 | REPLICAS

T HOUGH there are innumerable colloidal materials which it is instructive to examine with the electron microscope and its related techniques, solids are undoubtedly the most important objects for study. For an understanding of solid bodies and their physical properties we require as much information as possible about the composition and dimensions of their structural units and about the intimate relationships that necessarily exist between these units, whatever they may be. We are becoming increasingly proficient in the thin sectioning of solids, but most of what the electron microscope has told has come from the investigation of the surfaces of solids which have been subjected to chemical treatments of one sort or another. Under certain conditions these surfaces can themselves be examined, but most information is derived from the study of replicas taken from them. Numerous ways of making replicas that are suitable for electron microscopy have been described. No one type or technique of preparation can be selected as superior to all others because some work well on one kind of surface and some on another. Success in investigating a particular solid frequently depends on selecting the most suitable replicating procedure. Metals are perhaps the easiest to examine. They have been widely studied using a variety of these procedures, with results that represent a direct and obvious extension of the optical metallography which has been a major source of the knowledge we now have of alloy systems. For metallographic study a polished metallic surface is etched with an acid or other reagent to bring out the outlines of the separate crystals that make it up (Plate II). This etch pattern thus shows the distribution and grain size of the several components of an alloy. Many of these components etch in characteristic ways which serve to identify them; the etch patterns obtained before and after thermal or mechanical treatments therefore reflect the chemical and micro-crystalline changes that have taken place. The evidence the electron microscope can give reveals crystalline constituents too minute for optical visibility as well as those components that concentrate in the narrow boundaries between large crystalline grains; it also renders visible the fine-textured slips and deformations, often nearly down to atomic dimensions, that metallic crystals undergo when worked or stressed.

Metallic surfaces are prepared for replication by the same kind of polishing and etching required for direct optical examination, the only difference being that the etch should be much lighter if the replica is to be viewed at electron microscopic magnifications. In the early days of electron microscopy fear was often expressed that replicas would not reproduce the fine structure of surfaces with sufficient faithfulness to justify their use. It has now been amply demonstrated that this is not the case and that a properly made replica can be accurate to better than 50 A. There is, however, much uncertainty about what the electron microscope shows in many replicas unless they have first been shadowed. When a replica is formed its thickness will vary from point to point in a way that may not be simply related to the surface detail. The contrast thus introduced cannot be satisfactorily interpreted. It is one of the major advantages of shadowing that it eliminates these uncertainties by creating a strong contrast only on that side of the replica which bears the imprint of the etched detail (Plate II).

Methods to make replicas for electron microscopy fall into

two main groups, depending on whether or not the surface must be preserved intact. If it and the underlying sample can be sacrificed, the exceedingly thin replicating film may be formed directly on it. This is done most simply by pouring a suitably dilute solution of collodion, formvar, or other plastic over the surface and letting it evaporate to form a coherent film; the sample can then be removed under conditions that leave the film floating on the surface of the dissolving liquid. A more rugged and less easily deformed replica will be made by evaporating silica (or "silicon monoxide") or preferably carbon onto the solid and freeing this film in a like manner. Such detached films must be washed by transfer to one or more fresh water surfaces. Since the replica sides are downwards, grids are laid on the films and the combination picked from the water. After drying, these are then metal-shadowed for examination. Single-stage replicas of this sort were much used in the early days of electron microscopy when more complex techniques capable of preserving the specimen were imperfectly developed. They are not now so necessary except when the surface of a soft and friable solid is to be studied. Very informative replicas can, for instance, thus be made of bulk clays; they show the fragile crystalline constituents without the fragmentation that usually occurs when a clay is dispersed for direct examination. In this case the best replicating film is of carbon; silica cannot be used since hydrofluoric acid must be employed as solvent for the clay sample.

Strikingly beautiful and faithful replicas are made of many metals, not by applying a film to the surface but by oxidizing it, dissolving away the underlying metal, and thus freeing a coherent film of oxide for examination. These oxide replicas (Plate V) are frequently employed in the study of alloys of aluminum or iron because they are devoid of a perceptible structure of their own at the highest electron microscopic magnifications and give a faithful reproduction of very rough surfaces. In the first case the film is of alumina, in the second of iron oxide. It is formed on ferrous alloys by immersing the polished and etched surface in molten sodium nitrate. The superficial oxidation of aluminum is best carried out electrolytically; if proper conditions of electrolyte and voltage are chosen the reaction will cease with a given thickness of the oxide layer. It can then be removed without extensive damage to the specimen by treatment with bichloride of mercury. Aluminum oxide replicas have added value because they can be prepared from many nonmetallic surfaces by first making a thick aluminum replica. After being stripped this is oxidized on its replicating surface and the excess metal dissolved away with acid.

Replicas are valuable for optical as well as electron microscopic examination. They are most conveniently made of plastic thick enough to be easily detached from the surface they reproduce. Such replicas, preferably of collodion, can be taken from all sorts of surfaces; they have their greatest value in the examination of objects that cannot because of size or inaccessibility be placed under a microscope. We have used them, for instance, to examine large metal surfaces and to study very extensively the superficial structure of teeth. They can be taken as impressions in a plastic film one side of which has been softened with acetone or a similar solvent; or, if maximum fidelity is desired, successive layers of the dissolved plastic can be applied to reach the requisite thickness. Shadowing is as effective in bringing out their detail as it is for electron microscopy, but the metal to use is different. It need not be heavy, and evaporated aluminum of a thickness that will render the replica partially opaque to visible light is particularly suitable (Plate VI a and b).

When a replica from a surface that must be preserved is desired for electron microscopy, the procedures are somewhat more complicated. They involve first making a replica which, like those for optical microscopy, is thick and sturdy enough to be pulled from the object. Next, either it is converted into a film thin enough for electron microscopic examination, as is done with the aluminum-alumina replicas just mentioned, or a second, thin replica is made of it. If the solid is sufficiently strong and accessible so that the requisite pressure can be applied, the first replication can be an imprint made in a block of a thermoplastic like polystyrene or polyethylene. This procedure was frequently followed in the earlier days of electron microscopy but is rarely used now. The first replica is sometimes made by evaporating silver over the surface being studied. This film must be so thick that it peels with ease or it can be thinner and strengthened by an added layer of electro-deposited copper. After being stripped from the solid this thick metallic sheet is mounted with the replica side uppermost on a glass slide, and a thin second or positive replica made of it. This can be of collodion or other plastic, of evaporated silica, or perhaps best of all of evaporated carbon. The metallic negative is then dissolved away with nitric acid, leaving this positive to be washed, mounted on grids, and shadowed for examination.

It is usually more convenient to make the thick first replica of collodion. This should be built up as a succession of thin layers, using a dilute solution and pouring a fresh layer over the surface after the underlying layer has dried. When made in this fashion it can be pulled from even a relatively rough surface and will reproduce the detail there with very great faithfulness. Collodion is especially satisfactory for this purpose because, while it may tear, it does not flow and therefore deform under tension the way formvar, for instance, does. Such a thick replica tends to curl when freed, but it can be easily handled by tacking it replica-side up to a flat piece of glass (a microscope slide) using

55

small amounts of plastic cement. The thin positive to cover it is best made as a vertically evaporated film of carbon from which the collodion negative can be dissolved away with amyl acetate. As a final step the carbon positive is shadowed before observation (Fig. 16). If one prefers, the shadowing layer can be evap-

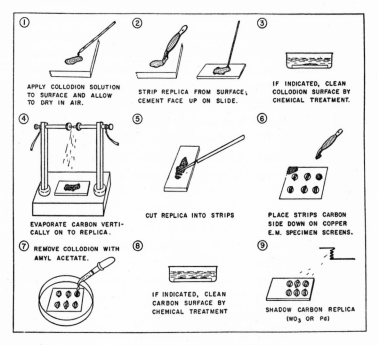

Fig. 16. A drawing to illustrate the steps involved in making a two-stage collodion-carbon replica. From D. B. Scott and R. W. G. Wyckoff, reference 11.

orated over the collodion negative before the vertical deposition of carbon. Such a "preshadowed" final replica is the same kind of composite metal-carbon film as is obtained by shadowing the carbon positive; though the application of the shadowing to the negative causes its hills and valleys to be reversed, experience has demonstrated that the two kinds of replica reveal the same micro detail. This collodion-carbon technique [11] is probably the most generally applicable of those thus far devised; it is accurate, and the strength of the initial collodion film permits the replication of wood (Plate VI d), paint, and surfaces too rough to be examined in any other way.

It can often provide more information than is contained in a simple replica. This is because, when pulled from a sufficiently rough or corroded surface, the thick collodion will frequently carry embedded in it some of the superficial layer of the solid. At least a part of this will be transferred to the carbon film and retained in it even after dissolution of the collodion. The resulting preparation (Plate VI c) is often too thick for electron microscopy at high resolution but it can be examined at low electron microscopic magnifications; and diffraction analyses carried out on the material entrapped in the carbon film will identify the crystalline substances that may be present. By restricting the area of sample yielding diffraction to a micro region (p. 49) the orientations of crystalline components as well as their chemical compositions can be established. For studies of their fine structure, such replicas can be treated with acid or other chemicals and, thus freed of attached fragments of sample, shadowed for observation at high resolution. We have used these combined replicas and "pseudoreplicas" to examine and analyze corroded surfaces and, as will be shown later, have found them invaluable in the study of teeth (p. 59).

Still further analytical information can be obtained from the bits of specimen in these pseudoreplicas. The electrons that strike them excite the fluorescent X rays characteristic of the chemical elements that are present. It is thus possible to make micro analyses for these elements by establishing the wave

57

lengths and the intensities of the emitted X rays. The potential usefulness of this technique is so great that its development will probably be rapid.

Teeth, which are biological in origin but largely inorganic in composition, offer a particularly instructive example of the more detailed approach to problems of fine structure that these electron microscopic techniques make possible. The teeth of mammals have three structural components: a central pulp which houses the blood and nerve supplies, an enveloping dentin made up of an intimate association of organic matter and poorly crystalline calcium phosphate, and the external enamel in which the calcium phosphate is well crystallized. Electron microscopy has already supplied much new information about the microstructure of dentin and enamel and the relation between their organic and inorganic components [12]. Years ago X-ray diffraction confirmed earlier conclusions that the calcium phosphate of the enamel has the same composition and atomic arrangement as the mineral apatite. The dentin contains far more organic material and a calcium phosphate that does not give clearcut X-ray diffraction patterns. Under the optical microscope the enamel appears as a system of rods about 30 micra in diameter running in different directions in different parts of a tooth. Its individual crystals are too small and the organic material has too fine a texture to be visible in this instrument. At these low magnifications, the dentin has appeared as a structureless matrix through which run apparently empty tubules about ten micra in diameter. Electron microscopy has penetrated much more deeply into the fine structure of both enamel and dentin to give knowledge that is valuable in its own right and is furnishing an essential background to detailed studies of how teeth form and what happens when they decay. Work in this field began as a comparison of the structure visible on replicas of the surfaces of healthy teeth and of teeth in various stages of decay. These were examined as thick shadowed replicas under the optical microscope and as thin shadowed replicas under the higher magnifications of the electron microscope. Similar electron microscopic studies were made using replicas from slabs sawn through enamel and dentin polished and etched with acid and from the surfaces of fractured teeth. Plastic replicas formed on enamel surfaces and liberated by dissolution of the tooth with acid have shown networks of filaments revealing the rods but lying between as well as within them; these evidently are acid-resistant organic material made visible by dissolution of the apatite crystals among which they were distributed. The replicas similarly taken from dentin have shown membranous structures associated with the large tubules that are everywhere present in it, and filaments in the matrix that fills the space between the tubules; when sufficiently cleaned by the acid treatment, these filaments have the characteristic striations of collagen. In regions where decay is beginning these replicas have shown the partial breakdown of the enamel and often the bacterial penetration that follows.

Additional information about these structures, especially the enamel, is obtained from pseudoreplicas [11]. The carbon positives of enamel contain both the microcrystals of apatite oriented as in the tooth and the organic filaments that lie between. Crystals and filaments can be distinguished one from another since an acid treatment of the replica removes the apatite but not the organic fibers. Electron microscopy of the untreated pseudoreplica shows the individual crystals of apatite and their distribution within and between the enamel rods; if unshadowed or shadowed with tungsten oxide which is noncrystalline, limited area diffraction demonstrates the orientation of the apatite microcrystals in relation to the rods. Similar pseudoreplicas of dentin indicate the microstructure of its tubules and the relation between its connective tissue elements and the inorganic phosphate, but since the latter is not crystalline, diffraction is here of no help.

Studies of this type made of both healthy and defective tooth surfaces treated with a variety of chemical agents will show what changes, if any, they make in the enamel and what deposits they may form on it. In this way one can demonstrate, for instance, by combined electron microscopy and diffraction the exceedingly thin layer of calcium fluoride that forms on a tooth treated with sodium fluoride. By supplementing such experiments with controlled observations on how the surfaces etch, it is possible to determine if such chemical treatments modify their resistance to acid. Studies such as these of the surface properties of teeth and other solids can now be greatly extended by the examination of sectioned material; an indication of how this is beginning to contribute further to our knowledge of the structure and development of teeth will be given later (p. 92).

PLATES

Plate Ia. An electron micrograph of a motile bacterium common in the air. The organism itself is so thick that its contents are not visible, but the many flagella responsible for its motility are easily seen. In a few places their fine structure can be discerned. The magnification is 19,000 ×. From Labaw and Mosley, Biochim. et Biophys. Acta, 15, 325 (1954).

Plate Ib. Parts of several bacterial flagella photographed at a higher magnification to reveal their stringlike character. Different kinds of bacteria have spirals of different pitch. Magnification 50,000 ×. From ibid.

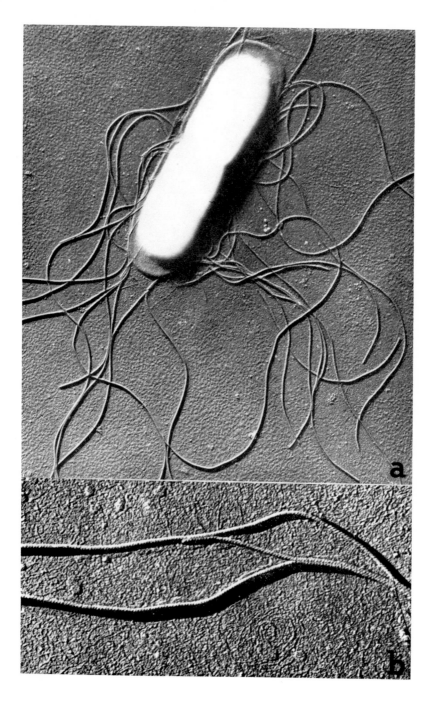

Plate II. An electron micrograph of a replica in plastic of the surface of a polished piece of the magnetic material ferroxdure. The elevations and depressions produced by the etching are made evident by metal-shadowing as described in Chapter 5. Photograph furnished by Philips Electronics, Inc.

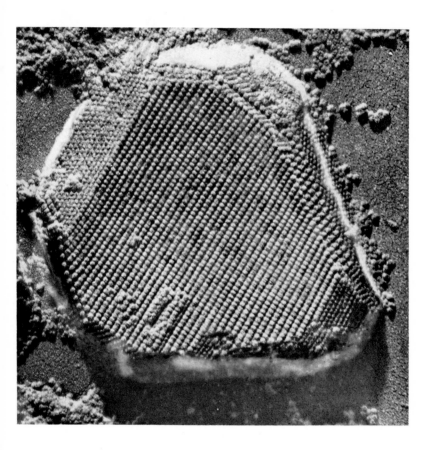

Plate III. An electron micrograph of the replica of a single crystal of the southern bean mosaic virus protein taken at a magnification high enough to reveal the ordered distribution of its spherical molecular particles. Magnification 50,000 ×. From Labaw and Wyckoff, Archives Biochem. Biophys., 67, 225 (1957).

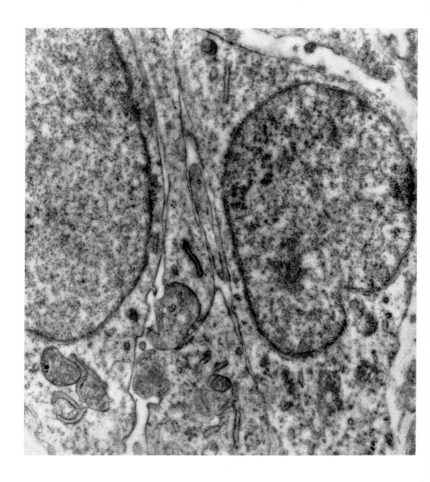

Plate IV. An electron micrograph of a thin section of a tissue that has been fixed in osmic acid and embedded in methacrylate plastic. Parts of several cells are visible. The large bodies at the two sides, each surrounded by its double membrane, are the nuclei of two of these cells. Magnification 17,000 ×.

Plate V. A replica of the etched surface of an iron alloy obtained by oxidizing this surface and liberating the film thus produced. Detail is visible because electrons must traverse different thicknesses of film and not as in Plate II because of a subsequent shadowing.

Plate VIa. An optical micrograph of an aluminum-shadowed thick collodion (negative) replica of a brass plate that has been roughly turned in the lathe. Magnification 90 ×. From Wyckoff, Electron Microscopy, (Interscience Pub., 1949), p. 99.

Plate VIb. A similar optical micrograph of an aluminum-shadowed plastic replica taken from a copper rotogravure printing cylinder. Magnification 70 ×. From Scott, Photogrammetric Engineering, April 1956.

Plate VIc. An electron micrograph of a tungsten oxide-shadowed carbon replica taken from a collodion pseudoreplica of a painted surface. The small square crystals visible here are the pigment crystals themselves. Limited area electron diffraction will give patterns by which they can be identified. Magnification 5000 ×. From Scott and Wyckoff, J. Roy. Micros. Soc., 75, 217 (1955).

Plate VId. An electron micrograph of the metal-shadowed carbon positive replica of a piece of pine. In the dotted regions the wood was cut transverse to its cellulose fibrils, but in the area between these the cut was nearly parallel to a bundle of the threadlike fibrils. Magnification 4500 ×. From ibid.

Plate VIIa. An electron micrograph of a thin section through portions of three cells of an onion root tip. Photographed without removal of the embedding methacrylate. Compare with VIIb. Magnification 20,000 ×.

Plate VIIb. A micrograph of a section of tissue similar to that of VIIa. In this case the methacrylate has been removed and the tissue fragments thus exposed have been lightly shadowed before electron microscopy. Some cellular details, notably the thick cell walls, the developing starch grains, and the occasional cellulosic fibrils, are better seen in VIIb than in VIIa. Magnification 20,000 ×.

Plate VIIc. The chromosomes of a dividing cell in onion root tip fixed in a strongly acid fixative of the sort conventionally used for optical microscopic examination. Magnification 10,000 ×.

Plate VIId. Chromosomes like those of VIIc in a section through onion root tip fixed in the neutral buffered osmic fixative now commonly employed for electron microscopy. The destructive changes produced by acid are evident from comparison with VIIc. Magnification 10,000 ×.

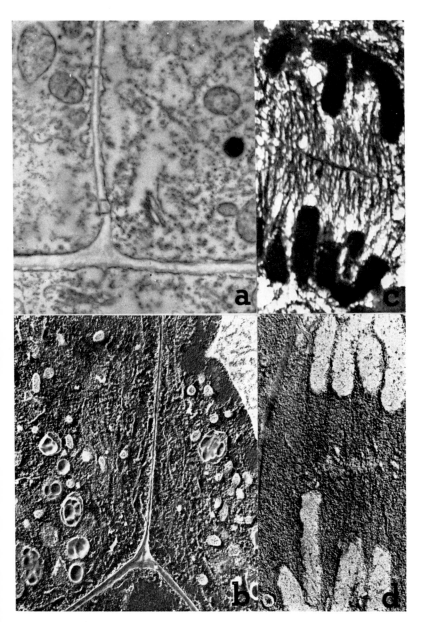

Plate VIIIa. An electron micrograph of a thin section of the epithelial layer of chicken embryo allantoic membrane which has proliferated after inoculation with vaccine virus. The nuclei are visible in five of the cells. Plastic retained. Magnification 4500 ×.

Plate VIIIb. A section similar to that of VIIIa but with the embedding plastic removed followed by a light metal-shadowing. Similar cellular details are visible in the two preparations but with different emphasis. Note especially the delicate links that connect the partly separated cells. The long white lines are defects due to a slight wrinkling of the section. Magnification 3800 ×.

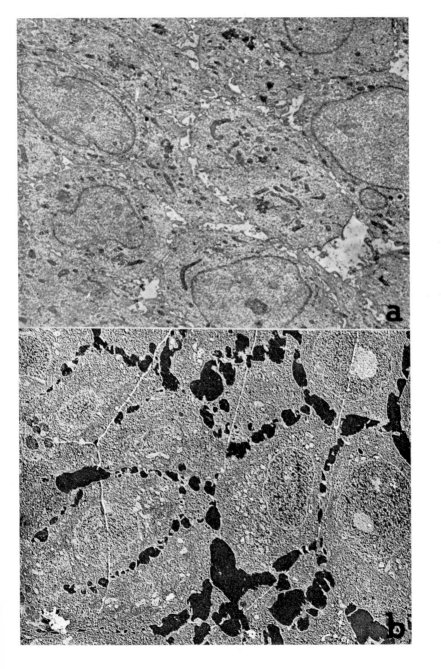

Plate IXa. A thin section through a cell showing several mitochondria, several opaque fat bodies of irregular shape, and several folds of cytoplasmic reticulum. Part of the nucleus with its denser nucleolus is at the top. Magnification 17,000 ×.

Plate IXb. A section through a similar cell seen at lower magnification. For comparison with IXc. Plastic retained. Magnification 5500 ×.

Plate IXc. A section through a cell similar to that of IXb but with plastic removed and a subsequent metal-shadowing. The substantial nature of the reticular membranes and the dilute contents of the space between the pairs of membranes are better seen than in IXa and b. Magnification 7500 ×.

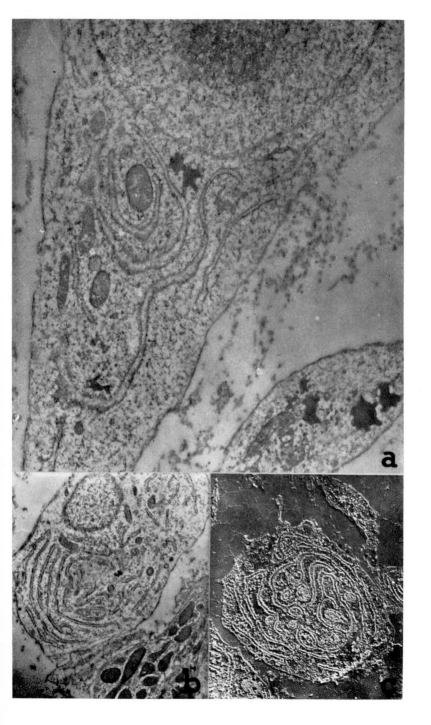

Plate Xa. Several tobacco mosaic virus protein rods lying on a carbon substrate and metal-shadowed. In freshly extracted plant juice the rods have a uniform length of about 2800 Å, but, on standing, these associate irreversibly to yield filaments of indefinite lengths. Magnification 70,000 ×. Photograph by L. W. Labaw.

Plate Xb. A bundle of filaments of cellulose teased from the secondary wall of the marine plant valonia. The filaments are essentially uniform in diameter and of indefinite length. Magnification 70,000 ×.

Plate Xc. The inner surface of its enveloping membrane exposed by rupturing a bacterium. This surface consists in part of a layer of spherical particles arranged in an ordered square net. Magnification 70,000 ×. From Labaw and Mosley, op. cit.

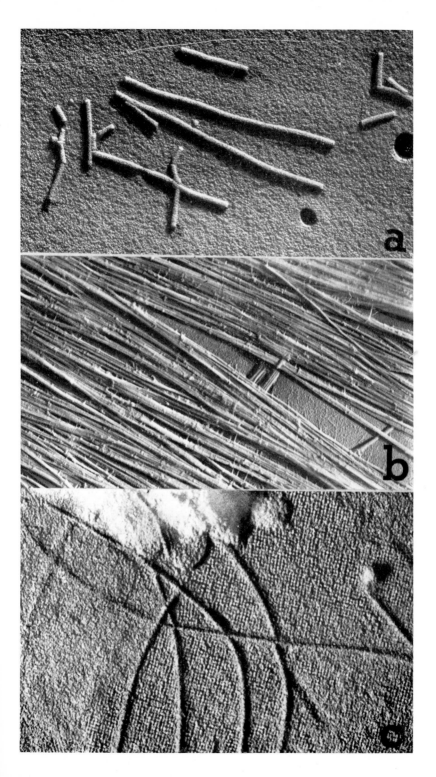

Plate XIa. A purified suspension of the elementary virus particles which are the causative agents of influenza. Most of these particles are spherical, but one particle in the lower right corner is a short rod. Rods, often very long and always of the same diameter as the spheres, are common with some viral strains. Magnification 40,000 ×.

Plate XIb. A purified suspension of the spermlike virus particles of the T6 strain of coli bacteriophage. Several collapsed heads and a number of particles which have lost their tails are visible. Magnification 70,000 ×.

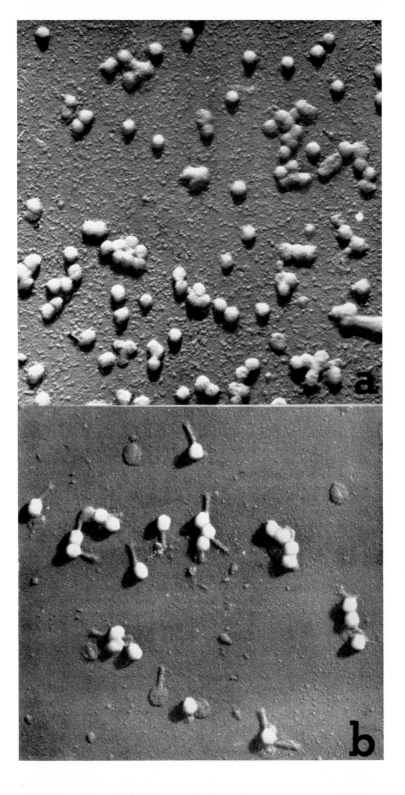

Plate XIIa. A section through part of the nucleus of a HeLa cell diseased with an APC virus, showing several packets of virus particles. Except in the immediate neighborhood of the packets the nuclear net seems relatively normal. The packing in the largest is almost tight enough to be crystalline. Plastic removed. Magnification 20,000 ×. From Croissant, Lépine, and Wyckoff.

Plate XIIb. One of the first sections cut through influenza-diseased tissue, which shows especially well how the virus filaments protrude from the cell borders before breaking off. Plastic removed. Magnification 10,000 ×. From Wyckoff, Nature, 168, 651 (1951).

Plate XIIc. Another early section of influenza-diseased tissue showing a mass of virus filaments and spheres along the border of the cell that has produced them. Plastic removed. Magnification 10,000 ×. From ibid.

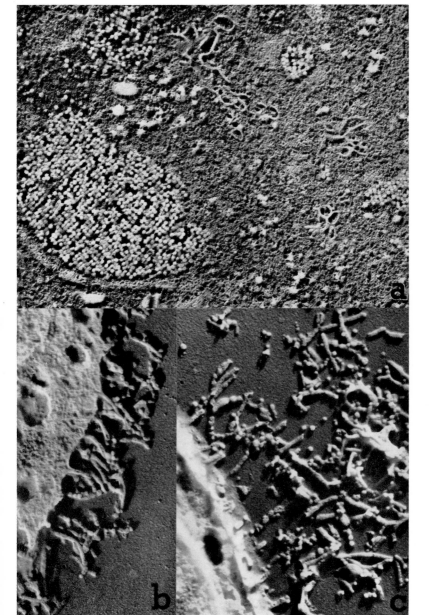

Plate XIIIa. A section through a vaccinia-diseased embryo membrane showing many of the newly developed virus particles (which appear here as white particles having dimensions of $\frac{1}{16}$ to $\frac{1}{8}$ inch). The large open spaces within cells are vacuolar regions produced by degeneration. Plastic removed. Magnification 7500 ×.

Plate XIIIb. A section through a vaccinia-diseased cell similar to that of XIIIa, showing many virus particles in various stages of development. The particles here appear dark. Plastic retained. Magnification 10,000 ×.

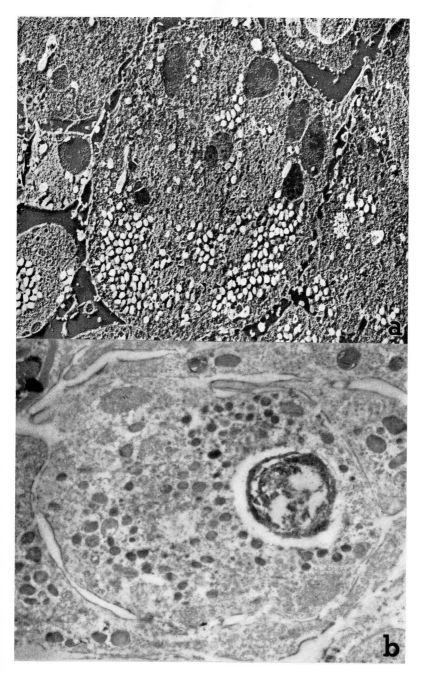

Plate XIVa. Collagen fibrils obtained by adding a slightly acid buffer to a clear collagen solution. The transverse ribs are 650 A apart, but fine structure is visible within and between them. Magnification 45,000 ×.

Plate XIVb. A fibril showing a periodicity in excess of 2000 A, obtained by dialyzing a collagen solution to which a trace of mucoprotein had been added. Magnification 18,000 ×.

Plate XIVc. Fibrils exhibiting a uniform 220 A striation, obtained by mixing a NaCl solution and a collagen solution. Magnification 28,000 ×.

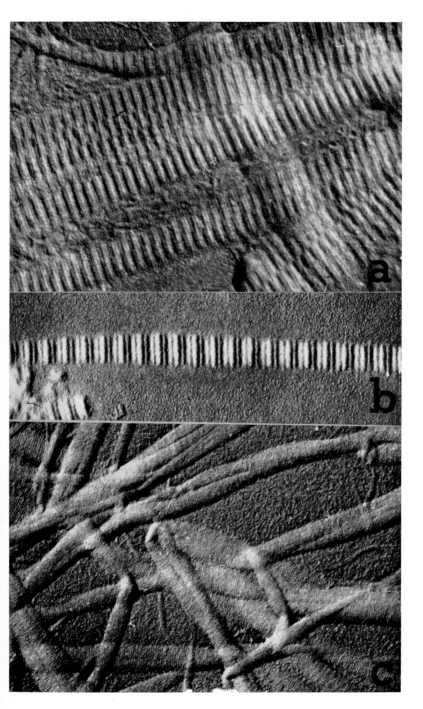

Plate XV*a*. An unusually perfect crystal of a tobacco necrosis virus protein. There is, however, a hole just left of center where one molecule on the top face is missing. Magnification 110,000 ×. From Labaw and Wyckoff.

Plate XV*b*. A far less perfect crystal of the tobacco necrosis virus protein showing several dislocations and other defects. That on the small crystal lying to the right of center is most obvious. Magnification 55,000 ×.

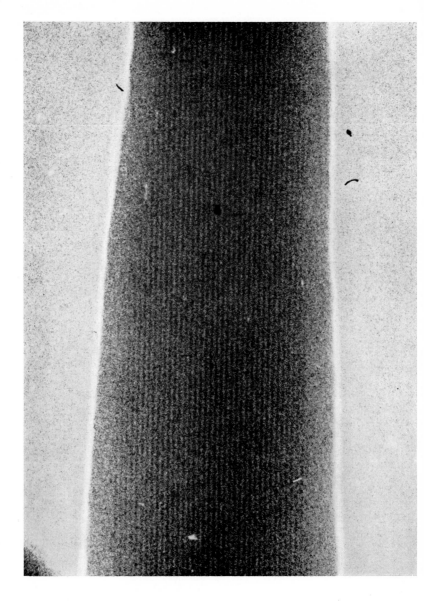

Plate XVI. An electron micrograph at very high magnification of part of a thin crystal of the dyestuff indanthrene scarlet showing the series of striations which may be interpreted as views along the molecular planes. The unstriated border is the contaminant built up on the crystal during less than a minute of observation. Magnification 750,000 ×. From Labaw and Wyckoff, Proc. Nat. Acad. Sci., Dec. 1957.

Chapter 8 | SOME OTHER ELECTRON OPTICAL METHODS

METALS, largely because of their good thermal and electrical conductivities, can be examined by a variety of electron optical techniques that supplement the transmission electron microscope. This can be done directly in a microscope having its illuminating system tilted at an angle to the axis of the rest of the column and the surface to be viewed placed in more or less the position it would have if it were reflecting electrons down this axis (Fig. 17). The electrons that produce an image in such a "reflecting microscope" [13] are not of course reflected by the

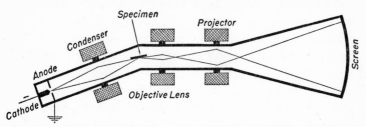

Fig. 17. A drawing which indicates the modification needed in the transmission electron microscope to adapt it to "reflection" microscopy.

sample in the sense that light would be reflected from a metallic surface; they are those scattered through such an angle as to be received by the objective lens. In order to use the more numerous electrons scattered through small angles, the angle of tilt has usually been kept small. Even under these circumstances most of the incident electrons are absorbed in the specimen and do not, as was the case with the transmission microscope, contribute to the image which is therefore formed only by the scattered electrons. A very intense beam is accordingly required to produce a visible image. The resolution in this image is comparatively low because so many of the electrons contributing to it will have been (incoherently) scattered with loss of energy. A serious disadvantage to reflection microscopy lies in the fact that, because parts of the surface examined are at different distances from the objective lens, the image is necessarily very distorted and, except for a narrow band, not in good focus. It has recently been found [14] that the angle of tilt can be increased considerably without serious loss of intensity and decline in resolution; this broadens the area of the image that is in approximate focus. An object viewed with this instrument produces an image of high contrast which emphasizes the surface relief and creates a very striking impression of depth. Instructive studies have been made of some metal surfaces and of textile fibers which have been metal-coated for examination, but the development of replicas whose faithfulness far exceeds the resolving power of the reflection microscope together with the three-dimensional information that can be obtained by shadowing has greatly curtailed the need for reflection microscopy and its useful applications. Nevertheless, there are developing fields to which it can make important contributions. It offers, for instance, a favorable experimental arrangement for combining microchemical analysis based on the emitted fluorescent X rays with an electron microscopic selection of the details to be analyzed. It is furthermore a way to study metals at elevated temperatures which should give information different from that to be gained either by emission microscopy (see below) or from replicas of quenched samples.

A fundamentally different kind of reflection electron microscope has recently been described which is now more interesting as an example of the diverse possibilities of our emerging electron optics than for the results it has yet produced [15]. In it slow-moving electrons are arrested in the potential field immediately in front of a piece of metal which is slightly more negative than the emitting cathode and "reflects" them back through the lenses of the instrument to form an image of the potential field and its irregularities. These irregularities can depend on such factors as the electrical conductivities of different parts of the sample as well as on its contours; whether or not it will be useful to "see" these potential distributions will depend on the future development of the instrument.

Electron microscopes have been built to form images using electrons emitted from the surface of a solid which acts as object. These are more highly developed than the "reflection" microscope just described but they have not yet been widely enough used to establish all the directions in which they may be expected to be of value. There are a number of ways to elicit electron emission from a solid; the information one obtains with an emission microscope and the application made of it will depend on the way in which the emission is brought about. No matter how this is done, contrast in the image is an expression of the relative efficiency with which different parts of the surface of the specimen are emitting electrons. In the emission microscope the electrons come either from the surface of the object heated to become an emitter [16] or from a surface that is either intensely bombarded with fast-moving charged atoms (positive ions) or strongly illuminated with ultraviolet light. In any case the freed electrons are accelerated by an impressed high voltage and formed into an image by the type of lens system employed in the transmission microscope (Fig. 18). In early days an attempt was made to study the distribution of metallic elements in biological tissues by incinerating them and examining the electrons drawn from the ash, but nearly all recent use of the emission microscope has been in metallography. Very few metals are copious emitters of electrons even at relatively high temperatures, and therefore in the thermionic type of emission microscope that is commercially available [17] the surface is ordinarily coated with a thin layer of a metal such as barium or cesium which becomes a good emitter at a moderate temperature. From such a coated metallic surface, the number of emitted electrons varies from point to point in a fashion determined by the chemical composition, the crystalline type, and the crystalline orientation of the underlying material; it is different for the different phases present and for the different crystal faces

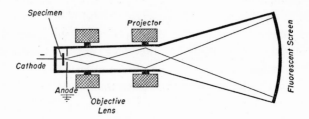

Fig. 18. In this simple type of emission electron microscope arrangement must be made to coat the face of the specimen *in vacuo* with barium or cesium and heat it to the temperature required for electron emission. If the electrons are evoked by positive ions, a suitable gun must be added which will produce a beam of such ions bombarding the specimen.

each exposes. As the temperature of the sample varies in the range through which its coated surface is emitting, the intensity of this emission delineates the minute details of phase transitions and crystal growth that occur. When barium or cesium is used the permissible range of temperatures lies between ca. 400° and 1200°C; the narrowness of this range is one of the limitations of the method. Less is known as yet about the possibilities of positive ion excitation [18]. It has the advantage that the sample need not be at an elevated temperature, but the damage produced by impact of the ions may be too severe to leave a wide field of usefulness. No matter how its electrons are liberated the emission microscope does not give an image of high resolution because of chromatic defects that have their origin in the considerable range of velocities with which the electrons leave the sample.

Another electron microscope built to give information about metals is the scanning microscope [19]. In such a microscope (Fig. 19) an extremely fine beam of electrons is made to travel in a regular pattern over the face of the specimen. The scattered

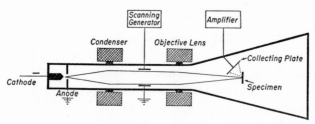

Fig. 19. The essential optical components of the "column" of a scanning electron microscope. The output of the scanning generator moves the fine pencil of electrons in a regular pattern over the face of the specimen. Electrons reaching the collecting plate from the specimen yield a signal for the amplifier. Its output impressed on a cathode ray oscilloscope (not shown) along with the scanning impulse writes on the oscilloscope screen the electron emission over the face of the specimen.

electrons are collected on an insulated plate, and the minute current they provide is amplified and impressed on a cathode ray tube synchronized with the scanning electron beam. The number of electrons scattered at any point of the specimen and the brightness produced on the screen of the tube will depend both on the way its contours are oriented toward the incident beam and on the chemical elements composing the illuminated point. This makes the image complicated to interpret but adds

65

to the information it contains. The resolving power is obviously set by the diameter of the scanning beam and hence is not high. This instrument could, however, be employed with specimens held over a wide range of temperatures, and its information concerning both structural detail and composition could rather simply be supplemented by observations on the simultaneously excited fluorescent X rays. Unfortunately scanning requires so complex an experimental arrangement that these data will probably be sought in some of the simpler ways that have been described.

The scanning microscope is but one of several types of electron optical instrument that utilize a sharply focused beam of electrons for microscopy or analysis. As the preceding discussion of electron diffraction (p. 47), has shown, these electron probes, as they are called, have great possibilities for the analysis of regions of microscopic area. Their full potentialities have not yet been realized because of the same contaminating layers that in the electron microscope interfere with work at high resolution. Nevertheless there are applications where contamination is less important.

Projection microscopes using an electron beam of minute cross section were built in the early days, but such shadow-microscopes had no obvious advantages over the better transmission microscopes that were soon constructed with lenses to magnify the image, and work was discontinued. The projection X-ray microscope [2] that is now attracting increasing attention is, however, technically only a minor variant of the early electron instrument (p. 19). It consisted of a pair of lenses so placed as to give a greatly demagnified image of the electron source, a specimen holder beyond the plane of this reduced image, and farther away a fluorescent screen and photographic plate to register the shadow of the specimen (Fig. 20). It becomes an X-ray microscope by placing a thin metallic foil in the plane of the reduced image of the beam to serve as target of the X-ray tube thus produced. X rays originating in this target will cast an enlarged shadow of the object on the screen or plate with a resolution that is approximately equal to the

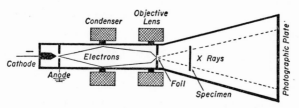

Fig. 20. The essential components of the projection X-ray microscope. If the thin foil which serves as X-ray source were not there the instrument would be a projection electron microscope. Unless the X rays are soft enough to be absorbed in air, the specimen chamber (to the right of the foil) need not be evacuated.

dimensions of the target spot. The initial magnification, as the ratio of the target-screen to the object-target distances, cannot be more than about one hundred because in the interests of intensity the distance from target to photographic plate should not be too great and it is impractical to bring the object too close to the target. By using fine-grained emulsions, however, all necessary enlargements can be made from the original photographs without loss of resolution. The smallest spot size and therefore the smallest details to be resolved are at present in the neighborhood of 0.1–0.2 micron; resolutions routinely to be obtained are perhaps from one-half to one micron. The instrument thus has about the same resolution as the optical microscope. There are many difficulties in greatly exceeding this performance and it is scarcely to be expected that the X-ray projection microscope will become in any sense a competitor of the electron microscope in seeing the very small. Its fields of usefulness lie elsewhere.

67

Important among these is the stereoscopic visualization of the inner structure of small objects. It is a characteristic of this lensless arrangement that, while changing the target-to-object distance alters its enlargement, the shadow remains sharp. As a consequence, all the inner details of an object appear clearly defined even when it is so thick that the side nearer the target appears with a considerably higher magnification than does the other side. The resulting distortion-in-depth is rarely troublesome, but the pair of photographs for stereoscopy are better taken by giving the object a lateral translation between exposures than by tilting it as is done in making stereoscopic photographs by electron microscopy. The sharpness of all detail contributes greatly to the remarkable vividness with which these photographs portray the spatial relationships of the contents of an object. The applications thus far made of this X-ray stereomicroscopy are mainly of an exploratory character, but the clarity with which it has revealed the crystallites in an alloy, the developing organs of an embryo, and the course of calcification of the bones and teeth of young mice suggests the value it should have in fields as remote from one another as metallography and embryology [20].

In another direction [21], projection microradiography is developing through the use of softer and more absorbable X rays. They are obtained by employing low excitation voltages and enclosing sample and photographic plate in a vacuum. With targets of aluminum or magnesium foil it is easy to make photographs full of detail from unstained tissue sections prepared by the conventional methods of histology and pathology. The use of these sections avoids the confusion of overlying detail that is seen in X-ray photographs of thicker specimens. Increasing the wave length of the X rays is also extending the analytical possibilities of X-ray microradiography. The different absorption of an element for X rays longer and shorter than its own characteristic radiation is helpful in identifying structures containing it; as the use of longer and longer wave lengths becomes possible this type of analysis can be applied to still lighter elements.

The micro focus X-ray tube that is the heart of the projection X-ray microscope unquestionably has other uses. Though the total energy in one of these micro beams of electrons may be small, the energy per unit cross section is very high indeed and the specific intensity of the emitted X rays correspondingly great. Such an intense X-ray source of minute area offers extensive but as yet unrealized possibilities for the X-ray analysis of minute quantities of material and for the study of the crystal structures of substances, including many proteins, which can form only tiny single crystals.

Chapter 9 | THIN SECTIONING

ALL THOUGHTFUL ATTEMPTS to apply the electron microscope to biological problems have been dominated by two considerations: a realization that much of what we see at its higher resolutions is at the macromolecular level of organization, and an appreciation of the importance of using methods that will permit examination of the most diverse forms of living matter at this level with a minimum of change from the organization that prevails in the living state. It was long ago clear that this could not be done using the conventional methods of cellular preservation. Very evidently the high resolving power of the microscope could be utilized only if we could find far less damaging fixatives for tissues and could devise effective means to cut sufficiently thin those sections that are the basis of cytology and histology. Before they became available, much preliminary information was gained through the examination of microorganisms, of the isolated cells of the blood, and of cells flattened by growth in tissue culture. But even the smallest organisms are too thick for observation at high resolution and they, too, must be examined in section if we wish to learn about the macromolecular details of their internal organization.

The tissue sections that are required for electron microscopy must be 200 A or less in thickness. It has taken several years to appreciate and master the technical difficulties met in cutting these slices that are more than two hundred times thinner than those routinely made for optical microscopy. They can now be prepared of soft tissues and sometimes of harder materials, though much more can be done to make cutting the thinnest sections routine. The first attempts were made about ten years ago, and at the time it appeared even more difficult than it has since turned out to be. Theoretical considerations had seemed to indicate that one could not reasonably hope to cut such uniform slices no more than a millionth of an inch thick with the knives and microtomes then extant. On the assumption that successful cutting would require very high speeds, attempts were made to use ultracentrifuge rotors with knives set in their peripheries. Such rather heroic efforts were uniformly unsuccessful —if thin sections ever were cut they were never recovered; and these experiments were promptly dropped when in 1948 it was demonstrated that only slightly modified conventional microtomes would furnish sections thin enough to put in the electron microscope. These first sections were still too thick for good electron microscopy but they encouraged the belief that the required thinness could be attained through further refinements. They also showed that tissues prepared by the best methods of classical cytology and histology were so severely damaged by the preparation that their examination at electron microscopic magnifications would be of little value. It was evident that a better preservation of the fine details of a tissue was as essential to successful electron microscopy as was the cutting of thinner sections. This is a problem that is far from its complete solution; nevertheless, the structure revealed in present-day electron microscopic preparations is certainly nearer to that which exists in the living state than what could be seen in the optical preparations upon which our classical knowledge of cells and tissues has been based.

The development of acceptable ways of cutting tissue sections thin enough for electron microscopy is a particularly intriguing example of how, even in these days of more and more complicated equipment, the successful solution to a difficult technical problem may be notable for its unexpected simplicity. For this reason as well as for the importance of the methods themselves it is worth describing their development in some detail. Three improvements in existing procedures were required before useful sections could be produced. One was to get a knife edge that would be sharp enough. This has been easier than at first expected, perhaps because it was not necessary to adhere to the shape of cutting edge and way of using it which mechanical theory has developed to guide the operation of lathes and other machine tools. Successful steel knives have been made by polishing both heavy microtome knives and thin safety razor blades, but the requisite quality has been given to only very short lengths of edge. To cut satisfactory thin sections this edge must obviously have no defects of a depth comparable with the thickness (less than one millionth of an inch) of the section. This exacting demand requires polishing against a smooth glass surface, using a polishing agent with particles so small that they cannot introduce such defects. Best results have been obtained with gamma-alumina as abrasive, but the good regions of a knife are rarely as much as a tenth of a millimeter long; they must be sought and marked for use while inspecting the blade under a suitably arranged optical microscope at a magnification of at least 750 times. These regions are very easily damaged, are difficult to preserve from corrosion, and have at best only a limited life when cutting. Thus, though sufficiently thin sections of very small area can be cut with steel knives, the process is so difficult and time-consuming that better knives are required.

They have rather surprisingly been supplied by pieces of broken glass [22]. Many kinds of glass do not yield good knives, and the required characteristics depend so much on both composition and treatment during manufacture that satisfactory batches of glass must be selected through actual trial. The knives are made as needed, by first breaking one-quarter inch thick plate glass into strips about an inch wide and then breaking these to yield pieces whose large faces are parallelograms about two inches long and have an acute angle of 60°. The quality of the knife edge depends as much on the way these breaks are made as on the quality of the glass. With some practice, however, the critical second break can be regularly made by pulling the glass apart after proper scoring. Only one edge is useful and most of it is defective. If the glass is good, examination under the optical microscope at high magnification will reveal at least a continuous millimeter and a half entirely free of the checkmarks that interrupt the rest of its length. These glass knives are brittle, easily chipped, and do not last long in use. Nevertheless, they are sturdy enough for sectioning soft tissues and have been used successfully to cut somewhat harder materials. They are cheap and easy enough to make so that frequent replacement is not too great a hardship. Much time is spent, however, in selecting their satisfactory regions, mounting them, and replacing them as they become damaged. For these reasons as well as because there are innumerable harder biological and inorganic materials which one would like to study, still better knives are needed. Thus it would be desirable to be able to cut routinely, instead of only occasionally, such materials as connective tissue, textile fibers, and rubber as well as calcified bone and teeth.

Several attempts have been made to meet these demands by cleaving and polishing hard crystalline substances such as sapphire and diamond. The efforts to do this with sapphires have consistently failed, but good diamond edges have been produced. These have cut satisfactorily thin individual sections of copper and aluminum and similarly hard materials without being damaged and seem to have a practically indefinite life if handled carefully. Most have not, however, had the acute-angled edge required to cut serial sections. When diamond knives of this shape can be made routinely they will unquestionably replace those of glass.

The second problem has been to obtain a microtome that could cut series of uniform sections of the requisite extreme thinness. Numerous designs have been described. Most microtomes cut by having a fixed knife and advancing the specimen between strokes by the thickness of the section to be made. It is hard to provide a uniform mechanical advance of less than a millionth of an inch. For one thing the films of oil necessary to lubricate moving parts are at least as thick as this, and for another only small thermal inhomogeneities and changes are sufficient to produce dimensional alterations of this magnitude in the apparatus. Microtomes which advance the specimen mechanically are being used to give satisfactory ultrathin sections, but results of notable uniformity are obtained when the advance is thermal. Initially this was done by chilling the support for the specimen and cutting as this metal warmed up. Results are easier to control if an insulated section of the specimen support is electrically warmed as cutting proceeds.

Ultrathin sections can barely be detected by eye under the best conditions of illumination, and this makes them both difficult and trying to handle. The relatively thick sections on which early work was carried out were easier to see and substantial enough so that using a hair as implement they could be picked up one by one from the knife as cut and transferred to a liquid surface on which they could straighten out. This is not possible with thinner sections; they must be allowed to float off onto a liquid surface as they are cut, collected there in ribbons or clusters, and transferred, washed, and mounted for microscopy, always using a droplet of liquid as transferring instrument.

In the conventional microtomes for optical microscopy the specimen usually moves vertically across the face of a fixed knife and is advanced at the top of each stroke for cutting on the next downstroke. When the advance is thermal rather than mechanical, expansion is continuous and the specimen on its upward path wipes vigorously against the knife. This does not necessarily damage either the specimen or the slightly flexible knife edge but it usually leaves the back of the specimen block wetted with liquid drawn by capillarity from the collecting trough. Sections already cut accompany the liquid and are thus lost. There are two ways to maintain the block dry between cuts: it can be done by giving the specimen a rotary motion that allows the upstroke to by-pass the knife, or either specimen or knife can be slightly retracted for the upstroke. Several successful microtomes [23] have been built especially for electron microscopy which operate on the first principle; those most familiar to American workers are the Sjöstrand and Porter-Blum instruments. Standard microtomes can easily be modified according to the second principle. This has been done for the Spencer rotary microtome, which is used in most biological laboratories in this country, by arranging automatic retraction of the specimen arm for each upstroke.

Microtomes of all these types will cut sections of the necessary thinness; some perform more consistently than others, however, and a choice between them must be based not so much on whether or not they can give suitable sections as on the regularity with which they do it. This is probably determined by the play that must exist in their oil-coated bearings and by their sensitivity to the vibrations to which they are subjected. Building vibrations that cannot be eliminated often have amplitudes many times greater than the thickness of the sections being cut and are thus an important cause of erratic sectioning. Some of the best microtomes are also the most sensitive to such external vibrations, a fact which must be taken seriously into account when selecting a microtome and arranging its mounting.

Considerable attention has already been given to the design
of instruments which, devoid of bearings and sliding parts,
would be free of this sensitivity [24]. In one type the specimen
arm is made flexible enough so that it can be bent sufficiently
on the upstroke to avoid the knife. In another the arm is rigidly
fixed to the base of the instrument by a horizontally placed
broad sheet of bronze and is moved up and down by bending
the sheet. Retraction is obtained by making a segment of the
arm of nickel, which is shrunk by magnetostriction during the
upstroke while at the same time the heat developed in the mag-
netostrictive coil gives the necessary thermal expansion. In instruments of still another design the specimen arm is rigidly
held and its motion controlled by two pairs of bronze sheets set
at right angles to one another. It is reasonable to hope that when
this development has been carried somewhat further an instrument of one of these types will evolve which will replace all the
others we now employ.

The third problem that had to be solved before satisfactory
ultrathin sections could be cut involved finding an embedding
material for tissue which could itself be sliced without fragmentation. The optical microscopist has used paraffin, or in some
instances a cellulose nitrate (celloidin), for this purpose. Paraffin crumbles if cut very thin, and early results with celloidin
were not encouraging. Ester waxes have been tried, but polymerized methacrylates have proved much superior and are now
almost universally employed. Tissue is embedded in methacrylate by first soaking a small piece, properly fixed and dehydrated,
in the liquid monomer; it is then placed in a capsule filled with
the viscous partly polymerized material, and the polymerization
is completed either by heating at about 40°C or by irradiation at
room temperature with ultraviolet light. The hardness of the
polymerized block depends on its composition; it can be altered
by choosing a different mixture of monomers. Presumably be-

cause they consist of filamentous molecules of very small diameter, the polymers have little apparent structure under the highest magnifications of the electron microscope; and because the molecules are in tangled masses, the thinnest sections show no tendency to shred or disintegrate, and they enmesh with little distortion the finest cellular details of the tissues throughout which their polymerization has taken place.

It has already been said that tissues prepared by the conventional methods of fixation appeared so seriously damaged when viewed under the electron microscope that better methods of preserving their fine detail had to be found before such examination would be worthwhile. The fixatives favored by the optical microscopist, whether based on formaldehyde, osmic acid, bichloride of mercury, or some other chemical, were strongly acid. The early attempts to improve tissue fixation for electron microscopy pointed to this acidity as the chief cause of the coarse coagulation so apparent under the electron microscope. When neutral and buffered fixatives were tried these coarse artifacts were replaced, no matter what the tissue, by a much finer, unbroken mesh in which the other constituents of the cellular protoplasm were enveloped (Plate VII c and d). Some neutral reagents yield more continuous and unbroken fine detail than others. At present osmic acid buffered to approximate neutrality is the basis for the most satisfactory fixative for general use. It is, however, reasonable to expect that still better fixatives will be developed now that the realization of their importance stimulates a broader search for them.

The demonstration by electron microscopy of how grossly damaged were the preparations of tissue considered adequate for optical microscopy has placed this problem of preparing biological material in a clearer light. It leads to a deeper consideration of how the chemical reactions involved in fixation probably alter the structural details of the living cell and of what

77

criteria we should establish for judging the amount of this alteration produced by different fixatives. It raises clearly the question of how good fixation is to be recognized when achieved. The evident advantage of neutral osmic over the older fixatives lies in the much finer and more uniform texture of the cellular structures it yields and in the fact that after treatment with it the various details of the cell lie enmeshed in and continuous with this protoplasmic net, without the obvious tears and breaks always present when the older optical microscopic preparations are viewed in the electron microscope. It is hard to escape the conclusion that this unbroken, fine structure is much nearer to that prevailing in the living state than what has previously been seen. Nevertheless, no matter how good fixation may be, the desiccation that must follow will certainly produce some changes of its own. Since there are of course no criteria for recognizing morphologically unaltered living structures, the final interpretation of much seen in electron micrographs should proceed slowly and with great caution. Only through experience gained by comparing a wide variety of tissues prepared by many different methods will we gradually and by degrees discover what the unaltered living structures are like. The investigation must be long drawn out and a test of both ingenuity and patience, but it cannot fail ultimately to yield a knowledge of the structure of living matter far more intimate than could ever have been attained without the electron microscope. From this knowledge of the macromolecular organization of cells will come help in understanding how they develop and how they fulfill their characteristic functions. It will equally supply the basis for all fruitful electron microscopic investigations of disease, since recognition of the characteristic changes brought about by a specific disease requires a thorough familiarity with the fine structure of the cells when healthy.

The observation of so much that is new tends to foster an

enthusiastic uncritical acceptance as fundamentally significant of everything seen in fixed tissue sections. Just as in the early days of optical cytology, naming all this new detail has become a serious matter to many people; and there is much speculation, some obviously farfetched, as to how it fits into what is known of the cell's intimate biochemistry. All this is healthy enough so long as nobody believes it too seriously and it does not, by giving a false sense of being well established, retard the urgently needed search for still better ways of specimen preparation. We cannot afford to lose sight of the fact that, while what we are seeing is unquestionably much nearer to what prevails in the living state, it is still a system of artifacts that are the products of the chemical interactions of the fixative with the reactive components of the tissue.

Some of the defects of our present methods of specimen preparation are so obvious that efforts to improve them need not be entirely blind. Nevertheless, we are faced with a central difficulty that we do not know how to avoid and that becomes more serious the better the tissue preservation. This is a consequence of two facts: (1) fixation must be immediate because cellular disintegration begins very promptly on death, and (2) the penetration of the fixative into the tissue, and hence the fixation of all but superficial layers, becomes slower the finer the texture of the already fixed material. These two considerations are in obvious opposition to one another. With some of the more delicate and labile tissues, such as brain, disintegration and the loss of fine structure that is its consequence may be so rapid that the fixative should be introduced into the animal while alive; this requires perfusion by way of one or more of the major blood vessels. Even when this is done the second factor operates so strongly with an osmic fixative that adequate tissue preservation often does not extend throughout an entire organ. Since the loss of structure that accompanies death has the character of a self-digestion due to the enzymes of the tissue, chilling before death may be a better brake on these chemical reactions than on the penetration of the fixing fluid. There are many interesting experiments to be carried out in this direction, including work with animals that, like hamsters, can be made to hibernate at will.

The most evident defect in tissues as now prepared for electron microscopic examination is the shrinkage they have undergone. Some of this occurs during the fixation, but most during the dehydration that follows. There are several procedures that might minimize this shrinkage and the distortions it must carry with it. Of these the substitution of other drying agents such as cellosolve or pyridine for the usual graded series of alcohol-water mixtures has not thus far been very helpful. The theoretical advantages to be expected by drying from the frozen condition have led to numerous attempts to make tissue preparations for electron microscopy in this way; it should effectively avoid shrinkage. Unfortunately, the damage to be seen in tissues prepared by freeze-drying has thus far been much greater than in those dried by chemical displacement of their water. This could be due to the greater fragility of the unshrunken residues, and part of it could be caused by the volume changes that would accompany the formation and growth of ice crystals during freezing or before drying has been completed. Any technique of freeze-drying which avoided this tissue damage would be an advance of the greatest value to all studies of fine structure.

Another source of possible damage lies in the considerable (about 20%) change in volume that accompanies polymerization of the methacrylates being used for embedding. It can be minimized by placing the monomer-soaked tissue in partly polymerized methacrylate and carrying out the final stages of polymerization at a temperature which keeps the plastic soft. There are other methacrylates which are less easy to handle but which do not change as much in volume when they harden; perhaps it will be possible to use them instead of the butyl methacrylate with which most current work is done. Interest is also turning to the epoxy resins, which polymerize with little shrinkage. Their use has made it possible to see structures within sectioned bacteria [25] which are otherwise lost and it may be that, in spite of several undesirable characteristics, these resins will prove preferable to the methacrylates for some tissues.

It is harder to see in what direction to turn for better fixatives. We may hope that reagents will be found which will produce a still finer protein coagulation than does osmic acid. Compounds should also be sought that contain heavy elements and will combine specifically with fine details of the cell and thus label them as do the stains of optical microscopy. Otherwise unseen detail has been brought out by treating connective tissue with phosphotungstic acid, but this is about the only example thus far of successful "electron staining."

Success in cutting sections of the utmost thinness has brought with it an interesting and curious limitation. In these thinnest sections there often remain so few of the cellular contents that unbroken contact between them is lost, together with a sense of the relationships they have to one another. In other words sections can now be cut that are too thin to contain the maximum amount of reliable information. This makes it often desirable to examine specimens of more than one thickness. Some should be thick enough to reveal the interconnections of the cellular detail and the breaks in these interconnections that occur if the tissue has been poorly fixed or otherwise damaged during preparation. They are particularly useful in the surveys of large areas of tissue that ought to precede all investigations at high magnification. Such thicker sections—perhaps two or three times that of the thinnest—scatter too many electrons for examination at high resolutions even after removal of the embedding material. All such examination must be of especially thin sections in order to minimize this scattering, to reduce interference between overlying details, and to separate closely associated structures.

In the past there has been rather pointless discussion as to whether or not the embedding plastic should be removed from a section before examination. There is always some distillation of the plastic from a preparation as it heats up under the electron beam, and this is greater the thicker the section. Probably methacrylate is never more than partially removed by the electron bombardment, however, because irradiation promptly encases the specimen in a layer of contaminating material that arrests distillation of the remaining plastic. When thick sections are to be examined it is better to remove the methacrylate chemically before they are introduced into the microscope. This can be done without disturbance and damage to the most delicate cellular structures if a slow-acting solvent like amyl acetate is employed. Very often, though not always, lightly shadowing a section devoid of plastic will add much to the information it can yield. The different and complementary character of what can be seen in sections of the same tissue prepared in these different ways is illustrated in Plates VII a and b and VIII a and b.

Rarely, if ever, is it desirable to remove the plastic chemically from ultrathin sections to be studied at highest resolution. The increase in contrast that occurs during the first few moments of observation of such a section in the microscope results from the volatilization of some of its methacrylate; but enough always remains to provide a generally distributed base for the contaminating deposit that is forming. This shields fine detail from direct contact with the deposit and preserves its sharpness from the rapid deterioration that is apparent in preparations from which plastic has first been removed.

Chapter 10 | SOME RESULTS FROM THIN SECTIONING

IT WILL require years merely to explore the greatly extended cytology and histology that are made inevitable by our newly acquired ability to examine thin tissue sections with the electron microscope; and many more years will be needed to put them on a firm basis. The observations of the last four or five years, by a very few people looking at a severely limited range of tissues, could scarcely do more than point to some of the types of microstructure that become visible at electron microscopic resolutions. Very little of this early exploratory work has been carried out by those older experienced cytologists and pathologists who know cells and tissues as the optical microscope has revealed them. Most has been due to the efforts of a few young cytologists and of others interested in certain diseases which cannot be understood through optical studies. From these rather mixed origins there are gradually accumulating those observations on the macromolecular texture of many sorts of tissue necessary as the basis for specific investigations.

This accumulation and classification naturally proceeds in two stages. The most interesting electron microscopic magnifications are so high and as a consequence the fields of observation are so restricted that a preliminary survey is needed to establish a firm relationship between what a tissue looks like under the electron and the optical microscopes. Such a survey requires electron micrographs not of small parts of a single cell but of considerable areas of tissue at magnifications comparable with

83

those used in optical microscopy. Now that the design of our electron microscopes permits the taking of distortion-free pictures at low magnifications, such a comparative study should be made with every new tissue to reconcile the often striking differences that exist between a conventionally fixed and stained specimen and the same material better fixed but unstained and very thinly sectioned for electron microscopy. Having made this identification, electron microscopists will naturally be chiefly concerned with those new features of the cell that are to be seen only at high resolution. Nevertheless, the electron micrographs made of large areas of tissue at low electron magnifications are so much clearer than the comparable micrographs made at high optical magnifications that we may also expect an increasing use of the electron microscope in histology. It is so much easier to make a first-rate electron micrograph at 3000 times magnification than a good optical micrograph at half this enlargement that once the development of microtomes for ultrathin sectioning has been carried somewhat further, electron microscopy will inevitably begin to replace the optical microscope in some of its routine applications.

Some of the newly seen microstructure of cells [26] occurs so generally that we are commencing to expect to find it in all sorts of tissues. There is thus a remarkable uniformity in the texture of the protoplasmic net wherever it is encountered (of course after neutral osmic fixation), with characteristic differences to be noted between the cytoplasm and the nuclear protoplasm. Equally characteristic structure is also becoming generally recognized for the membranous details of cells. We have, for instance, come to expect a doubling of many of the enveloping membranes, not alone of the cell itself but of its nucleus (Plate IV) and its mitochondria. There is also recognition of the more or less universal occurrence of membranous or sheetlike structures both within the formed mitochondria and free within the cytoplasm of a cell. In the mitochondria they have been named cristae, in the cytoplasm, endoplasmic reticulum. It has been difficult to be certain of the true configuration of these organelles because of the various ways in which they are necessarily sectioned and the extreme thinness of the preparations in which they must be studied. Sometimes they have appeared as a ladderlike succession of membranes, sometimes (Plate IX) as thin slabs enclosed within paired membranes of large area. Their function has naturally been a source of much speculation, but it is reasonable to presume they are closely connected with the intense enzymatic activity of the mitochondria and of the cytoplasm. Such slabs or sheets may be electronically somewhat more opaque than their surroundings while actually containing less matter (Plate IX c). They and the so-called Golgi apparatus, which is identified as a pleomorphic cluster of less opaque objects, are nowadays the most discussed of the new detail. A more definite understanding of their relation to the cell's essential chemical reactions may be expected from further studies of how their fine structures vary with cellular function and state of physiological activity. Once these relations are clear, the examination of how such presumed centers of chemical activity are modified by degenerative and other disease will become a fascinating source of new information about both the normal and the pathological life of the cell. Mitochondria, some of the larger sheets, and the Golgi apparatus are big enough to have been recognized before the days of electron microscopy; this is true, too, of the opaque lipochondria and the microsomes of various sizes found in the cytoplasm of many cells. The electron microscope is necessary, however, to reveal whatever fine structure any of these possess. Many cells contain innumerable minute opaque globules that may be either cytoplasmic or nuclear. The nucleoli of many but not of all cells appear to be aggregates of such particles; clustered about elements of the endoplasmic reticulum, they seem to constitute the Nissl bodies that are so distinctive a feature of neurons of the central nervous system as seen with the optical microscope. The exceedingly high electron scattering of these particles and their distribution suggest that at least some may be rich in nucleoprotein. This makes them of particular interest to students of viruses as well as to all others who are concerned with the activities of the nucleic acids of the cell.

There are several directions in which this new study of the microstructure of cells and tissues may be expected to proceed. Cytologists are extending their observations to more and more types of cells and concentrating on those that show in greatest detail the new structures the electron microscope has revealed [7]. The unusual emphasis that has been put on cells of the liver and pancreas with their many large mitochondria is in line with this [27]. Other investigators interested in the normal and pathological functioning of specific organs and tissues have begun to survey the microstructures that can be seen in them. Work has thus been begun on the kidney, the lung, and the stomach, on various glandular tissues, and on the skin; more comprehensive investigations have been made of the eye as an organ of sensation [28], of muscle [29] and tendon, and of the central nervous system [30]. Highly organized structures like the eye with its rods and cones, and muscle with its repetitive striae and filamentous elements arranged in orderly fashion, yield photographs of extraordinary beauty.

The almost startling improvement in the preservation of nervous tissue that can be achieved by the better methods required for electron microscopy makes its detailed investigation one of unusual promise. The complexity of what becomes visible is, however, so great that it is also one of extreme difficulty. With nervous tissue, the contacts that cells make with one another are of pre-eminent interest since it presumably is through them that impulses move to create the infinitely complex total reactions which the central nervous system characteristically produces. Even to begin to understand them will require the investigation of intercellular relationships with a care and on a scale not needed for most other tissues. Such an investigation must be based on an unusually extensive electron microscopic survey of brain and other central nervous system tissues at low magnifications. This atlas of large-area photographs is as necessary to an adequate understanding of the microstructure of brain and cord as are high-resolution pictures of its finer details. The features of overwhelming interest in nervous tissue are of course the nerve fibers extending to all parts of the body and terminating in muscle and organs of sensation, and the neurons of the central nervous system which are the foci of nervous activity and in which these nerve fibers originate. The large myelinated nerves were early made the object of electron microscopic studies and with each improvement in technique for specimen preparation this examination has been repeated. We now have a good understanding of the protoplasmic texture of the central axon enveloped by a myelin sheath that consists of layer after layer of lipoid-containing material [31]. Excellent photographs have also been published showing the intimate details of the relation of these fibers to the Swann cells which surround and nourish them. There remains, however, the need to know much more about the nodal regions that occur at intervals along a myelinated fiber and are certainly essential to the transmission of the impulses it carries; and, furthermore, we have as yet only an imperfect picture of how nerves terminate in the sensory organs and the muscles they control [32].

In the brain and spinal cord the neurons are the centers of interest. Their most distinctive intracellular feature is Nissl substance, consisting, as already stated, of great numbers of strongly scattering particles which especially in some animals are associated with endoplasmic reticulum. Where this occurs it is more conspicuous in Nissl bodies close to the nucleus and is difficult to find in and near the dendrite. The dendrite is an un-interrupted extension of the cell covered with the same very thin membrane as the rest of the neuron. We have yet to see how it becomes a myelinated nerve fiber. In the gray matter where they occur, most neurons lie quite separate from one another in a matrix of protoplasm which seems to be the widely pervasive cytoplasm of the so-called glial cells. There are other cells, too, interspersed with the neurons and glial cells, which are easily distinguished from one another in the electron micro-scope but are often hard to identify with those in optical prep-arations. Their functions have not yet been adequately estab-lished. These various types of cell do not form the kind of closely knit associations which constitute the tissues of most organs; they are found distributed among a mass of fibrous processes ranging from the large dendrites down to threads less than 1000 A in diameter. Most of them, large and small, are enclosed in membranes as thin as those of cells, but some have dense, thick-ened walls that presumably are of myelin. Each neuron makes contact with several thousand of these fibers, there being very little of its entire surface which is not thus involved. Many of the fibers appear swollen where they make contact, and contain an accumulation of mitochondria. Undoubtedly it is here that there is transmission of the nervous impulse from cell to cell. A few electron micrographs of these sites have been made at high magnifications, but prolonged investigation will be re-quired to show their fine structure and whether or not it is in any visible way different for fresh and exhausted nerves.

The older acid fixatives did, if anything, even more damage to the contacts between cells than to intracellular structures; and since in the central nervous system it is the relation between cells that is of paramount importance, the shrinkage, distortion, and breaking of cellular contacts which are such conspicuous features of acid-fixed tissues have been especially unfortunate. Such defects are absent from good electron microscopic preparations.

The electron microscopy of sectioned plant tissues can be as rewarding as the study of those of animal origin. From a technical standpoint, the best work to date has dealt with the chloroplasts, which are the centers of metabolic activity in the cells of leaves [33]. Photographs of well-fixed material thinly sectioned show that the grana of which these chloroplasts are composed are orderly stackings of sheets that scatter electrons strongly. Though they are much more extensive, these stackings somewhat suggest the endoplasmic reticulum of animal cells and thus provide another example of the close association of opaque, very possibly nucleoprotein-containing, membranes with centers of the intense metabolic activities of a cell. Their careful examination in vigorously growing, in resting, and in diseased leaves will undoubtedly throw light on this association.

The structural element of plants which quite naturally has received first and greatest attention is cellulose. Its elementary particles as seen within the tissues that produce them are indefinitely long macromolecular filaments (Plate X b). The electron microscope shows them individually and their arrangement, and it can demonstrate how they are formed. They can be seen and studied as produced extracellularly by certain microorganisms, but most attention has been given to their occurrence within plants. The cellulosic walls of plant cells consist of two parts: (a) a primary wall, the first to be laid down, which is a thin, tangled mat of these filaments, and (b) a secondary wall composed of successive layers in each of which the filaments are in parallel array. Sometimes the secondary wall is relatively thin, as in the stems of plants like cotton and flax that are the source of commercial fibers; in wood it practically fills the cells of which

89

it was at first only part of the covering. The visibility of the individual filaments in the electron microscope makes it possible to discover how they are distributed in fibers of different origins and thus to correlate physical characteristics with these distributions. Something of the various arrangements can be seen in preparations made by macerating fragments of wood and textile fibers, but much more can be learned from sections cut through the plants producing these fibers and through the softer woods. Replicas and pseudoreplicas prepared from the harder woods for comparison with these show in similar detail their elementary filaments and how they are arranged (Plate VI d). By working with young plants it will be feasible to see how these fibers are laid down and how the distribution of those already produced changes with the continuing growth of the plant [34]. A beginning has been made with the simple marine plant valonia.

It is known from X-ray diffraction measurements that the fibers of cellulose are partly but probably not completely crystalline. The attempts that have been made to see the regions of crystallinity with the electron microscope have not been successful. Some information about the internal structure of the individual filaments has, however, been gained by examining the fragments produced by treatment with chemicals like acid and hydrogen peroxide which will disintegrate cellulose. Partial studies have also been published of the "dissolution" of cellulose and of its regeneration as carried out in making rayon. Such experiments bear on the microstructure of natural and synthetic textile fibers, which have been extensively investigated by those concerned with their manufacture [35]. The added resolving power of the electron microscope is here useful for what it can show about the surfaces of such fibers as they occur in nature or are produced by spinning, as they are altered by wear and cleaning, as well as about their internal structure and the way they take up color when dyed.

It is inevitable that as use of the microscope expands it will be increasingly applied to questions of embryology and to the examination of tissues like the gonads which are in a state of continuous growth and multiplication. Mature spermatozoa were indeed among the early objects of electron microscopic examination, and their study has continued as our methods of specimen preparation have steadily improved. These investigations, which have had their stimulus mainly from the agricultural concern with cattle and fowl sperm, have had instructive results even though the heads of mammalian spermatozoa are so opaque that their internal structure is not revealed except in sections. The most interesting results have dealt with the elaborate microstructure of the midpiece which connects head with tail and of the tail itself. The tail, as seen best in cross section, has a complex structure which is especially remarkable for being practically identical with that found in the cilia of organisms phylogenetically far from birds and mammals, such as protozoa, both plant and animal, and the sperm cells of ferns [36]. All these cilia are clusters of eleven filaments embedded in a cementing matrix, with nine of the filaments arranged around the periphery of a circle that has the other two at its center. The internal structure of sperm heads is seen after sectioning mature sperm, but a far better idea of it has come from recent work showing the development of spermatozoa within the testicular tissue of the cat [37]. Such studies are valuable not only for the detailed information they give about how the elaborate components of a spermatozoan arise but for what they show about the microstructure of the cells of a vigorously metabolizing and proliferating tissue.

From the examination of such rapidly growing tissues, both

plant and animal, will inevitably come much new information about cell division [38]. The high resolutions of the electron microscope are sufficient to demonstrate how the nucleoproteins of the cell are mobilized to form the chromosomes, and to let us see what their macromolecular structure is and how it changes as the chromosomes divide and their chromatin is subsequently dispersed throughout the nuclei of daughter cells. Preliminary studies were made several years ago of the dividing cells in onion roots, and from time to time pictures have been published of other cells in division, but there has as yet been remarkably little work done considering the unquestionable fruitfulness of this way of approaching the structural characteristics of the nucleoproteins of the cell.

The evolution of our methods for sectioning tissues in course of development has made it possible to carry much farther the investigations begun years ago of the fine structure of teeth. Mature teeth cannot now be sectioned for electron microscopy without a preliminary demineralization, but forming teeth can be cut at all stages up to the point where calcification is about half complete. This is enabling us to study the macromolecular changes that occur in the cells producing a tooth, including the formation of the collagenous network of the dentin and the early stages in the deposition of the apatite of the enamel [39]. This apatite is first seen as well-formed minute crystals whose separate occurrence and orientation within the developing enamel rods can be observed by the same kind of combined electron microscopy and limited-area electron diffraction that was described in connection with the use of pseudoreplicas to examine mature teeth (p. 57). The final steps of calcification may be seen at low magnifications through the X-ray microscopy of sawed and ground slabs, and at high magnifications through the electron microscopy of thin sections after decalcification by acid. If this demineralization and the subsequent embedding are carried out with great care the small quantities of residual organic matter are sufficiently dispersed to preserve the outlines of the tooth structure in the fragile residue. Much is now being learned from such organic "skeletons" of teeth.

Chapter 11 | BACTERIAL AND VIRAL SUSPENSIONS

VIRUSES illustrate as do few other biological systems the way the visibility of microstructure alters the approach we can make to unique problems presented by living matter. From a technical standpoint examination began with their photography in purified suspensions and thus is in a sense an extension of what can be learned first about isolated cells and then about microorganisms of progressively smaller size.

Before the development of thin sectioning the only cells that could be examined under the electron microscope were either in single layers growing in tissue culture or those like the white and red cells of the blood which grow separately rather than in a tissue. Even when flattened by drying from the air after fixation these cells were always too thick for an adequate visualization of their internal structures. This was also true of the larger microorganisms, including the yeasts and molds. More could be seen about the contents of spirochetes and the smaller bacteria. The work done on them has accordingly contributed to our knowledge of their morphological characteristics and especially of their flagellar appendages, which were at best hard to see under the optical microscope. Some of this new knowledge [40] has been at the macromolecular level in revealing, for instance, bacterial protoplasm that consists largely of uniform macromolecular particles, bacterial membranes that look as if they were sheets of such particles in orderly array (Plate X c), and bacterial flagella that exactly resemble pieces of string (Plate I b).

94

Nevertheless even small microorganisms are too thick unless flattened, and this flattening may seriously disturb their inner structures. Satisfactory answers to such questions as exactly how bacteriophage develops within infected bacteria and whether or not bacteria actually possess nuclei analogous to those of higher forms of life cannot come from flattened cells. The internal details of bacteria as well as of larger free-living cells therefore must be studied after they have been fixed, embedded, and sectioned by the techniques devised for tissues. The examination of bacteria after sectioning has demonstrated that perhaps because of their thick cell walls they are even harder to fix properly than are more highly organized cells [41]. What has been seen depends so much on fixation and even on the type of embedding medium that electron microscopy cannot thus far be taken to have demonstrated the existence of bacterial nuclei. Still less is it legitimate to accept the coarse artifacts seen by optical examination as proof that we are seeing nuclei. The question of whether or not bacterial nuclei exist, and more generally, of how much organization there actually is within the protoplasmic contents of microorganisms must come from further improvements in methods of fixation and embedding and from the careful electron microscopy of such material after sectioning.

There are microorganisms, of which the pleuropneumonia group and some rickettsiae are best known, that are not much bigger than some viruses. They require the higher resolutions of the electron microscope for precise description of their shapes and internal structure. Several examinations have been made [42] of such transitional objects but these cannot be said to have done more than render clearly visible the pleomorphism already recognized with the optical microscope. For the viruses themselves the electron microscope has already had a far greater and quite revolutionary significance.

Viruses became an object of increasing scientific interest a generation ago as the presumptive causes of a group of infectious diseases which had to be attributed to particles too small to be recognized in optical microscopes and which required living cells for their proliferation. Relatively little progress toward understanding particles possessing such properties could be made through the use of the methods that had been so successful with bacterial disease. The need for techniques of a thoroughly new sort offered an exceptional opportunity to the biophysics which a generation ago was beginning to emerge. To these biophysicists viruses, considered then as the simplest forms of living matter, held a particular interest not as agents of disease but for what they seemed likely to tell about the living process itself. This has given the development of our knowledge of viruses a direction which it otherwise would not have taken.

From a biophysical standpoint this growth has proceeded in several steps. It started out with the recognition and then the purification of the elementary units of viral activity. When this had been accomplished one could then determine what they were like and measure their sizes and shapes. And finally with this preliminary information an attack could be made on the central problem of how virus particles arise within living cells and how their production influences the vital processes of these cells. Progress in all these steps has been substantial but in none has it been sufficient. It has been facilitated but at the same time rendered more complicated by the widespread character of virus infections—they are responsible for known disease in the higher plants and animals, in various insects, and in bacteria and some other microorganisms. As more is learned about them the viruses themselves appear as diverse as the forms of living matter they infect, and it is now clear that we will adequately understand what they are not after meticulously tracing the course of one virus infection but only after acquiring this knowledge about many different viruses.

Since particles of a virus are, by definition as well as in fact, too small for optical microscopic characterization, this kind of investigation of viruses could only get under way with the discovery of successful methods of purification. As interest developed it was first found that a few exceptionally stable plant viruses could be purified and even crystallized by the kind of chemical treatments that were then being devised for enzymes and other proteins. Most viruses are, however, rendered inactive by fractional precipitations with strong salt and other reagents. It was the failure of these chemical methods that made so valuable the successful use of quantity ultracentrifuges. Viruses of all sorts have now been purified, often in relatively large amounts, by this physical means, and these purified preparations employed to determine the sizes and general shapes of the particles of which they are composed. At first this, too, was done by ultracentrifugation, using the procedures that had recently been worked out to ascertain the dimensions of protein molecules. By 1940 we had come in this way to have a fairly accurate knowledge of the dimensions of the elementary particles of several viruses. This knowledge and experience provided the background for using the electron microscope to see what the particles in purified virus preparations actually looked like. What was first seen did little more than confirm the ultracentrifugal data; but since the development of shadowing the evidence of the electron microscope has become so direct, clear cut, and precise that it has largely replaced the ultracentrifuge as the way to establish the sizes of virus particles.

The viruses thus far observed have diverse shapes, and sizes that range all the way from the lower limit of optical visibility down to diameters less than those of some protein molecules. Many are spheres (Plate XI a), others are more or less elongated rods (Plate X a). Only the bacteriophages with their spermlike heads and tails have a more distinctive and complicated shape

97

(Plate XI b). The particles of most viruses are more or less deformed when dried from aqueous suspensions. The amount of deformation is as variable as are the sizes of virus particles. The smallest, with diameters of between 150 A and 300 A, are relatively dense and little flattened; this is equally true of many larger particles such as those of vaccinia and the rod-shaped insect viruses. Others like the particles of psittacosis and the large plant viruses are drastically flattened by drying and must have contents as fluid as tiny microorganisms.

The resolving power of the electron microscope is now great enough to reveal detail within and upon the surface of the particles of many viruses; for an understanding of what they are it is important to ascertain this detail as precisely as possible. Detail within particles that have been sectioned is either real structure or an artifact produced during specimen preparation. When it is superficial (Plate XV a) there are more possibilities. It can be real, or it can result from either changes in shape during drying or minute quantities of salt and other impurities nearly always present. Artifacts may also have been produced if there has been replication or shadowing. It is only safe to accept this micro detail as real when it can be obtained repeatedly and preferably under different conditions; it is not sufficient, as now frequently happens, to have a theory predicting microstructure and then be satisfied with the occasional observation that seems to justify it.

Current discussions about the shapes of the particles of some of the plant viruses illustrate this tendency to draw too facile conclusions. There has in particular been extensive debate based on very slight electron microscopic evidence concerning the fine structure of the tobacco mosaic virus rod. This virus protein when infectious contains about 4% of a nucleic acid which is rather easily removed. Prevailing hypotheses like to picture the virus particle as a long helix of the protein which, because of the symmetry of its X-ray diffractions, ought to be hexagonal in outline, with a hollow center for the nucleic acid. When viewed at high resolution most tobacco mosaic particles are approximately circular cylinders 150 A in diameter (Plate X a). As is true of other hydrated particles, shrinkage through drying often makes them appear vaguely polyhedral in outline. Sometimes they lack circular symmetry through a compression of their packed rods; sometimes it is demonstrably the result of an unsymmetrical accumulation of carbonaceous deposits. What appear to be fragments of these particles seen end-on have occasionally seemed polygonal in outline, and polyhedral shapes based on irregularities in the shadows cast have also been attributed to particles of spherical plant viruses. Very little impurity in a solution is sufficient to alter the shape of particles of macromolecular dimensions. If any of these viruses are really polyhedral, as may be the case, this must be demonstrated clearly and more consistently than has yet been done.

Other fine structure has sometimes been attributed to the tobacco mosaic rod. The helical model proposed for it repeats itself every 59 A. There is no evidence for such a repetition along most particles. This or some other spacing has occasionally been reported but without convincing demonstration that what was seen was not granulation of the shadowing material. To know the apparent shape of plant virus particles is especially important at this time. The number of plausible hypotheses we can now build about the shapes of the molecular particles of these and other proteins is vastly greater than the experimental data that can furnish conclusive evidence bearing on their validity. Electron microscopic visualization is one of the most direct sources of these data, but we will make genuine progress with its help only by accepting as established what the microscope proves beyond question.

More definite evidence of structure has been obtained from

the particles of other viruses. Thus the heads of certain bacteriophages appear polyhedral even after careful purification and drying from the frozen state, and the particles of the poxes in purified suspensions are remarkably bricklike. These and many other viruses also have internal structure that is easily seen though difficult to interpret. Many of the larger particles, including those of vaccinia, the bacteriophages, and the rod-shaped insect viruses, have enveloping membranes that can be observed in the intact particles and sometimes as residues after their rupture.

The electron microscopic examination of viruses is gradually providing interesting information pointing to the meshlike texture of the proteins that are their chief component. The large amounts of water present in particles of the smaller viruses can be removed without either their collapse or a shrinkage equivalent to the lost water. This suggests for them a spongelike structure. There is evidence that the nucleic acid content of these particles is sometimes similarly dispersed. An especially interesting example is the turnip yellows virus particle [43], which is spherical, has a diameter of about 210 A, and when infectious contains about 35% of nucleic acid. Through ultracentrifugation of a purified suspension a light fraction can be separated which is noninfectious and lacks this nucleic acid. Its particles are indistinguishable in size and shape from the infectious, nucleic acid-rich particles but are not as rigid and flatten much more when dried in air. The protein framework of this particle evidently is able to accommodate large quantities of both nucleic acid and water.

The success that has attended efforts to purify many viruses and see their elementary particles should not blind us to the fact that there are now instances where the attempts at purification have signally failed. Some of these failures have important contributions to make to our understanding of what viruses are.

Obviously a virus will be purified by ultracentrifugation only if it has the following attributes: it must be produced in relatively large amounts in the tissue it infects, it must be stable enough to withstand the isolation, and its particles must be approximately uniform in size. Some viruses have been difficult or impossible to purify because their host dies before they have sufficiently multiplied; others have been so reactive chemically that they have lost their infectiousness whenever attempts have been made to separate them from the debris of the cells producing them. There are, however, still others which have defied purification though stable and produced in comparatively large amounts. Presumably this is because they either do not differ significantly in dimensions from particles normally present in healthy tissues or lack the needed uniformity of particle size. Experience with virus in sectioned tissues permits increasing attention to viruses that are hard to purify. Sometimes it is found, as was the case with herpes simplex and the Rous tumor virus, that the probable virus can be recognized within infected cells even though its particles are not known from previous purification; in other instances, of which rabies is typical, the virus remains elusive. Any complete picture we may form of what viruses are must be able to explain this.

As SOON AS examination of purified preparations had made virus particles recognizable, a beginning could be made toward the next phase of their study—the search for them within the cells they disease and the attempt to see how they are there proliferated. Before satisfactory tissue sections could be cut, the scope of this effort was severely limited by the excessive thickness of intact cells. Bacteriophages received so much attention for several years because their particles were visible within infected bacteria. We were in fact restricted to them and to the very unsatisfactory observations that could be made on cultures of cells infected with virus. It is now possible to section and examine practically any virus-diseased tissue, plant or animal. Nevertheless not all such examinations are equally fruitful, and it remains true that significant results depend as much on the choice of material for study as on the quality of the electron micrographs that are made. This is not a field in which technical competence, necessary as it is, can replace a comprehensive view and sound understanding of the goal sought. Many viruses are highly selective in the kinds of cells they infect even within a particular host; a virus is far easier and usually more rewarding to study if we know the cells in which it is growing and can recognize its particles from previous examination of purified suspensions. Its development must be sought against the background of an adequate knowledge, at the electron microscopic level, of its host tissue when healthy, and the study must be very detailed if errors of interpretation are to be avoided. The virus-diseased tissues that can now be examined are so numerous that many years would be required to look at them all. What has been learned about one virus is not necessarily applicable to others even when the host tissue is the same; everything suggests that they differ as much in their development as in their particles. We have, however, learned much about how several important viruses develop and are beginning to understand what they are like.

What can be found out about any virus and its desirability as an object of study depend to a marked degree on the kind of tissue in which it must be cultivated. Plant viruses must be grown in their intact host plants. When they produce lesions that can be recognized early in an infection, the areas of tissue containing them can be selected for sectioning and infected regions found under the microscope without too much trouble. In this way tobacco mosaic virus has been observed growing within the cells of infected leaves [44] and the chloroplasts identified as the sites of the infection. With many other plant viruses the infection is less localized, and difficulty in finding the sites of growing virus is one reason why, in spite of widespread interest in purified suspensions, so little has yet been done toward seeing how their particles are produced.

There are many animal viruses which until very recently required cultivation in the animals that are their hosts; some must still be grown for electron microscopic study in organs of the intact animal. The insect viruses, for instance, can be cultivated only in the insects themselves. Animals are necessary as hosts when we wish to examine with the electron microscope how a neurotropic virus such as herpes or poliomyelitis grows in nervous tissue. They must also be used if we wish to understand the important effects a virus often has on cells other than those in which it is actually multiplying.

Many viruses of mammals and birds grow in chicken embryos and particularly in the chorioallantoic membranes that envelop them. For the electron microscopist these tissues diseased with virus have been especially favorable for study because here there has been but one simple host tissue to understand and because localization of the infection in it has greatly simplified the problem of finding virus-diseased cells. Most of the electron microscopy of developing viruses has used such diseased embryo membranes.

In the past, virus-diseased tissue cultures growing on cellophane have occasionally been embedded and sectioned as if they were membranes. Doing this can yield instructive preparations, but it is a difficult technique of rather limited applicability. The value of virus-diseased cultures as a basis for electron microscopic investigations has recently been much enhanced by several developments in the art of tissue culture: first, simplifications in the techniques and media of cultivation [52]; secondly, the discovery that quantities of added antibiotics sufficient to inhibit most bacterial infection do not interfere with cellular and viral growth; and thirdly, the observation that cells of a culture can be dispersed without damage into an easily manipulated suspension by brief digestion with trypsin. Combined with the new possibilities of working with cultures of a single type of cell having a uniform susceptibility to virus, these improvements are making tissue cultures the preferred means of virus cultivation for electron microscopic examination. In culture many viruses grow well in cells which they do not seem to infect in the intact animal. The use of cultures thus extends the material available for electron microscopy and simplifies even more than do embryo membranes the problem of obtaining the uniformly infected cells that can so greatly assist in tracing the course of virus production.

It would not be feasible to describe here all the observations that have recently been made on tissues infected with viruses and to discuss how they bear on the various theories about the nature of viruses that have from time to time been propounded. Instead a few observations will be used to indicate the general character of new knowledge which the electron microscope can provide and the change it is bringing about in the way we look at viruses and their problems.

It is appropriate to begin with bacteriophage because the bacterial viruses have been studied longer than most and by more investigators. Bacteriophages are very widespread in nature; strains have been isolated which infect and destroy many different kinds of microorganisms—bacilli and cocci, mycobacteria including some related to the tubercle bacillus, and molds such as those that produce penicillin. Nevertheless, most studies of how bacteriophage is produced have dealt with a few of the many strains to which the colon bacillus is susceptible. This virus system consisting of E. coli and the so-called T bacteriophages has been intensively studied by a wide variety of bacteriological and radiochemical techniques so that what the electron microscope shows can be coordinated with much other new knowledge. In discussing the properties of these T bacteriophages, however, it is necessary to realize that both they and the bacterial strain upon which they are usually grown have become highly specialized through prolonged laboratory cultivation and are in many ways not typical of freshly isolated bacteriophages and susceptible bacteria. The seven T bacteriophages are all spermlike objects but they differ considerably in their shapes and sizes, and an appreciation of these differences is necessary to an understanding of the complexity of the problem of what bacteriophages are. Those that have been given even numbers—T2, T4, T6—have heads 600–800 A in diameter and thick straight tails that are twice this length and about 150 A in diameter (Plate XI b). It has already been pointed out (p.

100) that their heads often appear more like hexagonal prisms than spheres. The heads of the odd-numbered strains are truly spherical. For T1 and T5 they are about 800 A in diameter, and the long and curved tails are much thinner than those of the even-numbered bacteriophages. The heads of the other two strains, T3 and T7, are smaller [45]. These have been reported to possess minute tails but usually none can be seen. A close study of the tails has been particularly important because of the role they have been shown to play in infection by the even-numbered bacteriophages. Chemical analysis of purified preparations of these bacteriophages shows them to be nucleoprotein in composition, but this analysis can be pushed farther as a result of the observation made several years ago that when distilled water is added to a pure saline suspension of the particles their heads rupture with the release of nucleic acid. The tails and the attached membranes of the deflated heads that remain —the "ghosts" of bacteriophage—are protein in composition; and there thus arises the picture of this virus particle as a sack of nucleic acid equipped with a tail [46].

The next step in the investigation involves finding out what happens when this particle infects a bacterium. It was early seen under the electron microscope that when growing bacteria were mixed with a suspension of any strain of bacteriophage to which they were sensitive the particles became attached to the bacteria. It has been hard to be sure of the manner of this attachment because drying-down in the air disturbs the mutual relationships. Critical point preparations (see p. 45) have, however, avoided this disturbance and have indicated that the even-numbered coli bacteriophages become attached by their tails to the cells. Soon after this the heads appear deflated. Experiments using bacteriophage having its nucleic acid labeled with radioactive phosphorus demonstrate that this acid passes to the bacterium it infects, and it has been inferred that it gets there through the attached tail, which is imagined as being hollow. This may well be the mechanism for infection with the thick-tailed bacteriophages; there is as yet no more direct proof of it nor information as to what takes place for tailless bacteriophages or those having tails which are very thin. Following infection, however it may take place, the bacterium continues to grow, but experiments with radioactive elements show that it is according to a new and different metabolic pattern. It does not divide after a certain amount of growth, as would a healthy bacterium, but swells larger and larger. After a period that depends on the strain of bacteriophage and the richness of the nutrient, its enveloping membrane bursts, and this is followed either immediately or after a time that may be as long as a couple of hours by the liberation of many new particles of bacteriophage; simultaneously the suspension becomes clear, or in other words it lyses. Bacteria, if they are of a susceptible strain, can also adsorb ruptured particles (ghosts), but when this happens they swell and burst without the formation of bacteriophage [47].

We do not now have any idea of how this protein of the virus arrests the cell division of its host. Evidently if virus particles are to be produced the nucleic acid of the bacteriophage must enter the bacterium, but this acid is not what stops the bacterial division. The swollen, infected cells soon become too thick for good electron microscopic observation, and what happens from this point on should be carefully investigated using sectioned organisms. A few photographs [48] that have been made show that this can be very instructive, but what has thus far been learned has come from observations on less satisfactory preparations that were suspensions of infected bacteria. It is especially significant that particles of bacteriophage have not been observed within a bacterium during the first half of the period of infection. Newly formed particles have become visible in rapidly mounting numbers within the bacterial protoplasm only in

the few minutes immediately before the cell lysis that has liberated them. During this period one sees many incompletely
formed particles—heads more or less devoid of contents or with
short, incomplete tails; under unfavorable conditions of growth
there will be produced masses of elongated tails that are without
heads, or membranes of heads having the form of ribbons and
devoid of tails. As bacteriophage particles develop, the character
of the bacterial protoplasm changes; especially after infection
with those bacteriophages that cause delayed lysis, the initially
particulate protoplasm of the bacterium is replaced by a fibrous
network. It is the slow disintegration of this net after rupture of
the cellular membranes which is responsible for the retarded
liberation of newly formed bacteriophages. This transformation
of the cellular protoplasm from globules to filaments, more or
less complete depending on the type of bacteriophage, draws
attention to the problem which besets all studies of how viruses
develop. This is learning how to distinguish the morphological
alterations leading directly to the formation of the particles of
virus from those pathological changes that in one form or another are to be seen in all sick and dying cells. The most difficult
aspect of this study of virus growth and the greatest possibility
of error lie in discriminating between these two distinct but
simultaneous processes; they can be separated only after prolonged and careful observations on many viruses and tissues.

The electron microscopy thus far carried out falls far short of
what is needed for a thoroughgoing understanding of bacteriophages as virus, but it makes clear what should next be done to
increase this understanding. Most needed is a detailed re-
examination of all stages in the infection of E. coli by the T
bacteriophages, using this time thinly sectioned organisms fixed
to preserve their inner structures better than heretofore. This
may add to our knowledge of the mechanism of infection and
will certainly indicate without the disturbances produced by the

previous bacterial flattenings the way forming bacteriophage particles are distributed throughout the cell and what their earliest stages look like. There must also be a further examination of the phenomena presented by the "lysogenic" bacteria which are so often the natural carriers of viral activity. They occur everywhere in nature, and laboratory cultures can be propagated indefinitely without lysis. Under normal conditions nearly all the bacteria in such a culture grow and multiply with no evidence of infection, but an occasional cell is always rupturing with the liberation of bacteriophage. Under suitably chosen conditions the entire culture will lyse with the same wholesale production and liberation of new bacteriophage that occur when susceptible bacteria and bacteriophage are incubated together. It can be demonstrated that these lysogenic phenomena are not due to the presence of a few infected bacteria among many resistant ones because all subcultures from single cells behave alike and carry the original ability to produce bacteriophage. Electron microscopy of cell suspensions does not reveal particles of formed or forming bacteriophage within lysogenic bacteria, as might be the case if they were carrying bacteriophage propagating too slowly to give more than occasional cell destruction but fast enough so that no newly divided bacteria were free of particles. Instead, the bacterial contents resemble those of infected bacteria before formed bacteriophage has begun to appear within them. It will be important to examine, also in sections, lysogenic bacteria that have grown both normally and under conditions that stimulate the widespread lysis of which they are capable.

Everything that the electron microscope has shown about bacteriophages is consistent with the idea that they are not independently living microorganisms parasitic on bacteria. They are rather to be imagined as packets of nucleic acid and protein which are slightly different chemically from those of the bac-

terium but can, when introduced into it, participate competi-
tively in its metabolic processes. Under the stimulus of the abnormal protein, growth continues but cell division is inhibited.
When the abnormal nucleic acid gains the upper hand, bacteriophage is produced; when its growth does not outstrip that of
the normal acid, it evidently can continue as a lysogenic possibility. Such an interpretation of course leaves much unsaid. It
does not, for example, explain why the changes within the
infected bacterium initiated by bacteriophage are so exactly
adapted to producing the elaborately organized viral entities,
all of whose parts are essential to the propagation of infection.
Nevertheless, what has been found clearly points to bacterial
virus disease as an altered, and lethal, metabolic pattern which
is passed to other, "normal," cells in the form of small fragments of the modified nucleic acid and protein.

There are other viruses that under electron microscopic scru-
tiny also appear to be abnormal products of a modified cellular
metabolism. Influenza and the viruses related to it are of this
character. They grow well in the allantoic and amniotic membranes of the chicken embryo under conditions that supply
excellent material for investigation. During this growth they
accumulate in large amounts in the fluids these membranes enclose and thus have been easy to purify by ultracentrifugation.
Influenza has been extensively studied under the electron microscope. In its purified preparations most of the infectious particles are spheres about 1000 A in diameter (Plate XI a), but
there are always also present filaments of the same diameter.
Some viral strains yield very few of these filaments; with others,
they tend to predominate. It is now evident that both the filaments and the spheres are elementary particles of the virus. The
examination of influenza-diseased chicken embryo membranes,
as well as of infected mouse lungs, was begun eight years ago [49]
as soon as it became technically possible to cut sections thin

enough for electron microscopy. The observations then made have been frequently repeated, with concordant results. Extensive examination failed to reveal within cells of infected tissue either the filaments or spheres that comprise the virus of the purified suspensions. Both are, however, found in abundance extending from the borders of the cells that line the membranes of the egg and the alveoli of the lungs. Here they appear as a profusion of filamentous processes developing from the surfaces of the cells, breaking off and frequently segmenting into chains of little spheres (Plate XII b and c). Relatively thick sections such as were employed in the early work often cut through the still-attached filaments and revealed their contents as continuous with the cytoplasm of the cells; evidently they began as part of the cells and not as extraneous entities proliferating along their borders. The fact that these filaments and spheres appeared indistinguishable from the particles in purified virus preparations, together with a consistent failure to find other particles of the right size elsewhere within cells of the infected tissues, has made it hard to avoid the conclusion that they are the developing particles of influenza virus. The same phenomena have been observed with the related Newcastle virus of birds [50].

The interpretation of the virus particles as detached fragments of the cytoplasm of diseased cells is supplemented by observations on membranes not infected with these viruses. Similar filaments develop, but usually do not detach, from the cells of noninfected membranes placed in an unfavorable environment. A few can usually be found on the borders of the membranes from most embryos, and after infection with viruses totally unrelated to influenza, such as vaccinia and herpes, they are produced in large numbers but are demonstrably not the infectious particles. Many types of cell, like the carcinomatous HeLa cells now widely used in tissue culture studies, have this capacity to form pseudopod-like filaments. From the wide range

111

of observations that have been made we seem compelled to conclude that the virus particles of influenza are such detached and segmented pseudopods of diseased cells.

The virus seen developing through the electron microscopic examination of tissues diseased with vaccinia, or any other of the numerous pox diseases, is entirely different from influenza in character and mode of growth. The bricklike particles, ca. 2000 A x 2000 A x 2500 A, that constitute the mature elementary bodies of these viruses are as easy to recognize within infected cells as in their purified suspensions. In fact this easy recognition has been made the basis for an effective method of early diagnosis that is valuable in those regions where the danger of smallpox is great [51]. Vaccinia, the cowpox with which most of us have been innoculated as protection against smallpox, grows readily on embryo membrane, giving there poxlike lesions in which the elementary particles are produced in large numbers [52]. The first response of a membrane to infection with vaccinia is not, however, cell destruction with the rapid production of virus particles but a vigorous proliferation of the epidermal layer of cells (Plate VIII) and an edematous accumulation of fluid in the mesodermal region beneath it. These areas are the characteristic swollen poxes. As infection proceeds, the new epithelial tissue begins to degenerate, cells of its outer layer become full of vacuoles, and its inner cells gradually separate one from another to float in the mesodermal fluid. Virus particles appear first, and often in great numbers, in the cytoplasm of these cells of the disintegrating tissue (Plate XIII). They are readily distinguished by being much more opaque to electrons than the other cellular contents. None of these opaque particles can be seen either when the cells are actively proliferating or later in those outer cells that show a pronounced fatty degeneration. When first recognizable, the virus particles occur separately or scattered in small groups through the cytoplasmic network that is beginning to disintegrate. Later this net may have almost completely disappeared, to leave the particles in massive aggregates that sometimes nearly fill the cytoplasmic space. Before the appearance of virus and during the early stages of its production these cells are seen to possess tiny mitochondria as well as the larger ones that are big enough to be visible in the optical microscope. They have the same enveloping membranes and on a diminutive scale the same internal structures that characterize the big ones. Many of the tiny mitochondria are short and have about the same diameter as the virus particles; when virus is beginning to be recognizable the thin sections contain numerous bodies which cannot positively be identified as one or the other. In the face of such evidence it is necessary seriously to entertain the possibility that the modified metabolic processes of the diseased cell stimulate the proliferation of these minute mitochondria which then become transformed into virus as the diseased cell disintegrates. It is to be hoped that the further study of this virus growing in other types of tissue will convincingly confirm or forbid such an interpretation. If the tiny mitochondria and the virus are related, then with the poxes, as with bacteriophage and influenza, virus is the product of an altered cellular metabolism. Unlike influenza which is derived from unorganized cytoplasm, vaccinia would arise from one of the cell's highly organized components.

There are many viruses that develop in the nucleus rather than in the cytoplasm of the cells they infect. We are beginning to learn how a number of them grow, and it is instructive to contrast the appearances of cells diseased with nuclear and with cytoplasmic viruses. Herpes simplex, the cause of fever blisters, is a nuclear virus which has been studied in a number of different tissues [53]. Its growth in chicken embryo membranes is particularly interesting because in them it produces many of the same cellular changes that follow infection with the cytoplasmic

113

vaccinia. An adequate understanding of infection with herpes has been rendered difficult by the fact that the form of its elementary particles has never been established through the examination of purified preparations. In chicken embryo membranes herpes gives rise to the same initial epithelial proliferation followed by fatty degeneration, the same mesodermal swelling and pox formation, and the same gradual detachment of the new epithelial cells into this edematous middle region of the membrane that is seen after infection with vaccinia. And virus forms in these cells as they start to disintegrate, as well as perhaps in invading leucocytes difficult to distinguish from them. The initial cellular changes are indeed so much the same that it is impossible to say before disintegration begins which has been the infecting virus. The proliferating epidermal layers even produce in both cases many of those filaments, with some spheres, that are noninfectious but morphologically like the virus particles of influenza. Once it has begun, the cellular degeneration due to herpes takes an entirely different course from that observed in the membranes infected with vaccinia. The first evidence for it is the accumulation of electronically dense material on the inner side of the periphery of the nucleus. Particles that resemble opaque droplets are often found singly and in little groups in the neighborhood of this material and elsewhere within the nuclear network. Thereafter the nuclear net seems to start breaking up and many of the particles are at first ringlike in appearance. Some, however, have opaque, strongly scattering centers, and later nearly all are dark-centered. It would be consistent with what has thus far been seen to consider these particles as accumulations of nucleic acid-containing material within pores of the disintegrating nuclear net. The same sequence of events leading to them has been traced in cells in the brains of rabbits and mice diseased with herpes and in

114

herpes-infected tissue cultures. It is very possible that they are virus. If so, herpes may be another disease like bacteriophage for which a modified nucleic acid or nucleoprotein is responsible.

Like those of herpes, the particles of poliomyelitis and its related viruses develop within the nuclei of infected cells, but in a totally different fashion [54]. The electron microscopic examination of purified preparations has demonstrated that the particles of poliomyelitis are spheres about 250 A in diameter. Cell nuclei that are little more than sacs full of such particles are to be seen in sections of the central nervous system of poliomyelitis-diseased mice and of diseased tissue cultures. Their identification as virus is supported by the fact that they occur nowhere else in these diseased tissues. Particles of similar size can, however, be seen within the interstices of the nuclear net of healthy cells of similar origin and they are present in the ultracentrifugal concentrates from healthy brain. There is thus nothing morphologically unique about the virus particles of poliomyelitis. From electron microscopic observation it is impossible to say if virus is a normal cellular component modified by disease and liberated by the attendant disintegration of the nuclear net, or if it is newly produced during disease; perhaps there is little real difference between these alternatives.

There are many viruses with infectious particles that are not in any evident way related to or developed from some element of the infected cell. It is amongst them that we should look for viruses that might be related to the world of microorganisms. The insect viruses that attack many kinds of caterpillar are of this sort [55]. Some are little rods which resemble bacteria in the organization they display. Within cells they are enveloped in a fluid menstruum that suggests a bacterial capsule; they have a well-defined membrane, and some exhibit dense inclusions like the spores by means of which many bacteria survive adverse conditions. We must ask if they are effectively tiny microorganisms or if the structural details we see and the crystalline polyhedra that ultimately enclose so many of the particles are both reactions of the diseased cells aimed unsuccessfully at isolating these lethal products of a metabolism gone astray. Very clearly we do not now have the information for an answer, but at least a better formulation of the question itself will surely be forthcoming once the requisite work has more fully outlined the course of these infections.

The recently identified APC viruses, which can be isolated so often from human adenoidal and tonsillar tissues carried in culture, in some respects also suggest microorganisms. Their elementary particles are spheres about 650 A in diameter; developing within cell nuclei, they have no counterpart in healthy cells [56]. As is not the case for other viruses studied, they can become exceedingly numerous within a cell without breakdown of the protoplasmic net surrounding them (Plate XII a). Their production must therefore be less toxic than usual to the cells in which they occur. Probably as a result of this proliferation without extensive cellular damage, they are often so tightly packed that they assume a strikingly ordered, crystalline arrangement. Examination of these crystalline packings gives no hint of how the particles have arisen, but the nonuniformity of particles in cells infected for relatively short times may be suggestive. A few are considerably bigger than average, and there are associations that strikingly recall microcolonies of coccoidal bacteria.

Some of the results discussed above demonstrate that there are viruses which must be considered as products of a modified pattern of cellular metabolism, with infectious agents that may be nucleic acid. Other results show that there is no present justification for concluding that all viruses are to be explained in this fashion. Fortunately many plant and animal viruses are accessible for study by the techniques now at hand. Their careful investigation is not a job to be quickly accomplished but it is the way to understand what viruses are. Rarely can information so important be sought with so great an assurance of success.

Purified viruses and those identified within diseased cells have, almost of necessity, had rather uniform and characteristically shaped elementary particles. As our insight into their nature becomes greater, more attention must be given to the viruses which have resisted attempts to purify them. Some of these do have uniform particles but they are trapped in tissue residues of indefinite size. This, for instance, is why the Rous virus which causes tumors in chickens cannot be purified until it has been liberated by enzymatic digestion from the gelatinous residues of the cells it has destroyed. When this is the explanation for failures to purify we should still be able to find, as was the case with herpes, the distinctive virus particles in sectioned, diseased tissue.

Rabies is particularly interesting in this connection because very careful study of diseased tissue has failed to reveal any fine detail that could be identified with particles of virus. Animals diseased with laboratory-adapted strains die without exhibiting characteristic cellular changes that point to the sites of virus proliferation. Freshly isolated, "street," rabies produces the Negri bodies which, as inclusions within cells of the nervous system, are our means of diagnosing it. These cells and their near neighbors have been meticulously examined on the natural expectation of finding virus within them. The Negri bodies, which are easy to recognize under the electron microscope [57], are not aggregates of virus-like particles, nor are such particles to be found elsewhere in these preparations. Only after excluding the possibility that the Negri bodies are a response to virus being propagated elsewhere in the animal can final conclusions be

117

drawn from such negative results. This is typical of those situations where virus cultivation in tissue culture could be of special value in providing uniform host cells for infection.

Though the knowledge we have gained about what viruses are, as illustrated by the foregoing examples, is still very fragmentary, it is beginning to have implications beyond the restricted field of virus research. The fact that some viruses are nucleoprotein fragments of a diseased cell and that others are abnormal nucleic acid elaborated by a sick cell should influence the way we think about all transmissible disease. Equally significant is our inability to recognize virus in cells rapidly multiplying in response to virus infection or in lysogenic bacteria. Such observations point to transformations in a cell's complement of nucleoprotein or nucleic acid which do not immediately yield virus-like particles or necessarily result in cellular destruction. It is not now possible to have a reasonable idea about the prevalence of such nonlethal transformations since in general we would remain unaware of them without especially designed experiments. We cannot, however, ignore the possibility that modifications of the nucleoproteins of a cell analogous to those that cause virus disease may be responsible for nonpathological, including embryological, cellular changes.

This is a matter which is quite obviously linked to the question, still completely speculative, of how viruses originate. Mutants are constantly arising among the cells that are hosts to viruses and amongst viruses themselves. This is, for instance, true of bacteria under laboratory cultivation and of bacteriophages that are propagated on them. More highly organized cells change their characteristics with time, and new strains of viruses often appear. Cancer cells seem recently to have been observed arising "spontaneously" within a normal culture. Such changed cells probably resemble some virus-diseased cells in having altered nucleoproteins; they differ in that the new metabolic pattern thus established is lethal in the case of virus-diseased cells but not for the others. After herpetic and vaccinial infection cells proliferate in the same uncontrolled fashion as do cancerous cells but they do not end in a tumor because of the disintegration that rapidly sets in. Such viral activity is, considered superficially, a sort of self-destroying cancer. In the few known cases, e.g., the rabbit papilloma in domestic rabbits, the Rous tumor in fowls, and the "milk factor" in mice, where viruses can be isolated as the cause of cancer, the connection between virus and tumor is not so direct. Viral transformations and those that might be direct causes of cancer are antithetic in their activities: the metabolic change expressed in virus disease is deadly for the cell but usually not for the organism; any transformation leading to cancer must be benign as far as the cell is concerned though the unrestrained growth it makes possible may kill the organism.

There is clearly room for much imaginative experimentation in the broad field of cellular transformation, which includes some viruses as one of its aspects. It is useless to speculate about the results, but it should be emphasized that the tools for such experimentation now exist. And it is important to the present discussion that the success the electron microscope has already had in dealing with viruses shows it to be one of these tools.

Chapter 13 | MACROMOLECULAR STRUCTURES

THE KIND of morphological study just illustrated by viruses will ultimately be carried out for many of the essential proteins and other macromolecular substances of healthy living matter. It will begin with observations and measurements on their macromolecules in purified solutions and then proceed to find these molecules within tissues and to see the way they are there produced and function. How difficult this will be will depend very largely on the size and the morphological distinctiveness of the molecular particles. Most of the macromolecules of healthy cells are smaller than virus particles, but there are some that are unusually big and these will undoubtedly continue to be favored on account of their easier visibility. Many of the macromolecules in nature are simple proteins, but more are complexes with such other macromolecular units as the nucleic acids, polysaccharides, and lipoids. These, too, occur by themselves or can be split from their protein complexes. Examples of each have been seen with the electron microscope, and the discussion of cellulose (p. 89) has suggested some of the possibilities the microscope presents.

The classification, proposed a generation ago, of the proteins as either globular or filamentous has been largely borne out by electron microscopic examination of their molecular particles. Most of the readily soluble proteins of nature, those that are excreted by the cells that make them and move about freely in the animal body, are globular. The digestive enzymes and the respiratory and serum proteins have such a shape. On the contrary, those proteins that make up the fixed structures of the body and constitute its organic solids usually have filamentous molecules. Most filamentous macromolecules, whether protein or not, do not have a uniform molecular weight in solution; they are indefinitely high multiples of a small chemical unit.

Electron micrographs have been made of many macromolecules in purified solution. For the more or less spherical molecules, our seeing them has not greatly modified the information about sizes and shapes which ultracentrifugal measurements had already supplied. Those thus far visualized reach down in size to diameters of about 40 A and weights of the order of 50,000. Occasionally genuine structure can be seen within these macromolecular particles. An early example is furnished by molecules of the hemocyanins, which are the respiratory proteins of many invertebrates. Long ago ultracentrifugation showed that the molecular weights of many were not constant; they changed with acidity by simple multiples of a basic unit. Electron micrographs have explained this for the hemocyanin of a sea snail, Busycon canaliculatum, by showing that its heavier molecules are aggregates of a few of the uniform little rods which are its molecules at another pH. As another more recent example [58], molecules of the smaller protein ferratin have a four-cornered inner structure that has been attributed to the distribution of their iron atoms.

Observations on filamentous particles in purified solutions have given much new information, since for them necessary corrections for particle shape make unreliable the interpretation of their rates of sedimentation in the ultracentrifuge. Such particles thinner than 40 A have been photographed but, as already pointed out in discussing tobacco mosaic (p. 98), impurities in the preparation and granulations of both substrate and shadowing material require a most conservative interpretation of the detail such particles may seem to possess. Nucleic acids are ex-

121

amples of substances having molecules that are exceedingly long filaments. The viscosities of their solutions vary so greatly with method of chemical preparation and subsequent handling that their ultracentrifugal data can give little reliable information about molecular dimensions. It is possible, however, to make electron micrographs of molecules that have undergone a minimum of alteration. In such preparations, including nucleic acid liberated directly on the specimen grid by rupture of the heads of bacteriophage, the molecular particles appear as indefinitely long thin threads perhaps 15 A in diameter [59].

The electron microscopic appearance of most filamentous macromolecules will usually be related to the solids they form. In contrast to those that are globular, filamentous molecules ordinarily do not crystallize either in nature or when extracted and purified. They do, however, associate together to form fibers and aggregates of fibers in which there is some order in the way the molecules are arranged. The physical properties of such fibrous solids are intimately related to this paracrystalline order. It is seen for the first time with the electron microscope, and that is why this instrument is so important to the study of tissues in which this order exists, like tendon, muscle, and the myelin of nerves.

Two steps in the formation of many of these fibrous solids contribute to the particle order they display. One is the organization of the molecular elements together to form fibers and sometimes sheets, within which the electron microscope may or may not reveal the molecular order. The second process, which is the organization of these fibers into two- or three-dimensional arrays and the sheets into three-dimensional stackings, may like the first be physicochemical but is usually brought about as part of the growth and development of living organisms.

The formation of elementary fibers from their smaller molecular constituents is frequently a polymeric association of these components. Cellulose fibrils must be formed by some such process from small carbohydrate molecules, but not enough has yet been seen to give a picture of what is thus happening everywhere in the plant world. A simple protein illustration of how fibrils are produced is the formation of filaments of fibrin from its precursor fibrinogen. The macromolecular particles that have been seen in preparations made from diluted, purified fibrinogen solutions are indefinitely long threads about 30 A in diameter. When fibrinogen is treated with thrombin it polymerizes, with the formation of filaments of fibrin. The blood clot that forms in the body is a tangled mesh of these filaments produced when fibrinogen in the blood reacts with thrombin liberated by the damaged tissue of a wound. The polymerized fibers of this fibrin are approximately uniform in diameter in any one preparation, and under the electron microscope each exhibits a fine structure which consists of cross striations or thickenings repeated every 250 A along its length. Similar striae characterize the polymers of many biologically important filamentous macromolecules. They are the consequence of some still-unknown feature of the molecules that regulates their association into filaments.

Collagen, as the basis of all connective tissue, has been an object of interest since the beginning of electron microscopy and is thus the most studied of these filament-forming substances. Its striated fibers as seen in tendon show a dominant band repeated every 650 A, with repetitive detail between bands that seems to depend somewhat on both the source of the material and the way it is fixed for observation. Most connective tissue has this fine structure.

The electron microscopic investigation of collagen has been rendered especially fruitful by the fact that in the laboratory its fibers can be dissolved and re-formed at will. Many years ago it was found that treatment of fresh tendon, especially from young

123

animals, with very weak organic acids yielded a highly viscous, clear solution from which a fibrous precipitate could be obtained by treating with salt. Later it was shown that such a precipitate gave the X-ray diffraction pattern of the original collagen. Still more recently the electron microscope has confirmed this identification by revealing that each new fiber bears the same 650 A striations as the tendon from which it was derived. The very long threads no more than 20 A in diameter to be seen in the solutions must be collagen molecules. Fibers are precipitated from these solutions by pH adjustment and dialysis as well as by salting-out, and several electron microscopic studies [60] have been made to see how these factors affect their fine structure. Addition of the collagen solution to buffers of different pH gives fibers of different shapes but always with the 650 A spacing of the original tendon (Plate XIV a). On the other hand, its addition to physiological saline often results in thin fibers that are banded with a uniform periodicity of only about 220 A (Plate XIV c). When the solution to which a minute quantity of a mucoprotein has been added is dialyzed against water, the fibers have a totally different periodicity in excess of 2000 A (Plate XIV b). There are evidently several ways in which the same collagen molecules can be aligned to form ordered fibers. Most of the collagen seen in nature has the 650 A banding of tendon; the uniformly striated fibrils of spacing ca. 220 A are the only other forms encountered. Further investigation of these fibrils and of the abnormally shaped fibers sometimes met in diseased and repaired tissues should ultimately be of help in understanding aspects of degenerative disease.

The repetitive structure of collagen fibers is evident in sections through connective tissue as well as in shredded fragments. Tendon is a difficult tissue to section, but this has been done with particularly instructive results. Longitudinal sections show that the fibers which are grouped parallel to one another in bundles often have their striae aligned in three dimensions. Transverse sections cutting through the individual fibers indicate many of them as hollow [61]. The thinner collagenous fibers of other forms of connective tissue have on the contrary appeared solid. Tendon is known to contain substances other than collagen and notably considerable quantities of polysaccharide. What the electron microscope shows therefore suggests that the fiber of tendon is a sheath of collagen around a core of some of this other material which has disappeared during specimen preparation.

This picture of the collagen of tendon fibers as a kind of sheath or skin corresponds to what is also seen in reprecipitated preparations. Large precipitated fibers are, unlike the small ones, very flat. Reprecipitation brought about directly on the specimen grid yields areas of striated order which spread as a sheet over the background between fiber-shaped elements and thus demonstrate that the molecules of collagen can arrange themselves to form a membrane as well as an elongated fiber.

There are other proteins that produce striated fibers strikingly like those of collagen but they have different spacings between their major striae and different patterns of fine detail. One of these proteins is the so-called light meromyosin [62] obtained from the muscle protein myosin by tryptic digestion. The distance between the striae of its fibers is 420 A, instead of the 650 A of collagen. Paramyosin from the clam is another protein associated with muscle having this type of fiber. It manifests a still more complicated structure: after fixation with phosphotungstic acid, its fibers show a two-dimensional pattern of spots instead of striae.

An indication of the kind of structural units that may guide filamentous macromolecules in their orderly groupings has been given by air-dried solutions of actin. This protein and the myosin just referred to are obtained by the cautious extraction of muscle. Evaporated from very dilute solutions, its molecules resemble those just discussed in being indefinitely long threads in which no certain fine detail is observed. When its solutions are sufficiently concentrated so that the molecular threads are in contact as they dry, they form parallel bundles in which some repetitive detail along the filaments is visible. There is here the suggestion that the isolated filaments consist of short, rodlike units attached end to end and that when the filaments pack the alignment of this substructure creates the two-dimensional order visible in the more concentrated deposits. The tendency illustrated by actin for short macromolecular rods to form long relatively stable threads by an end-to-end association is more clearly shown by the tobacco mosaic virus protein. Its 2700 A–long rods, brought into contact by concentration and standing, similarly associate to produce the long filaments that are the principal molecular constituents of old solutions. Perhaps future research will reveal for other substances analogous molecular subunits determining the repetitive order so characteristic of all these fibrous solids.

Probably most of the membranes essential to living organisms are composed of filamentous molecules. Their molecular components are in most cases too small to be visible, but the cell walls of plants illustrate on a gross scale what one might expect to see. The primary wall consisting of a tangled layer of filaments is a membrane. Animal membranes have not yet been found which, like secondary plant walls (p. 89), consist of well-ordered molecules. The membranes of some bacteria may be of this character (p. 94), though in this instance (Plate X c) the molecules appear spherical [40]. The layers that can be peeled from muscle are sheets of parallel filamentous macromolecules. Single membranes limiting a cell or one of its details are common, but we are coming to find more and more often that membranes occur in stacks. These may be only the double membranes that are being observed with increasing frequency as sections through tissue are cut thin enough to reveal their presence. We are, however, also finding that many of the most active centers of metabolic activity in cells are stacks of membranes. They are in fact not so much piled membranes as sandwiches, which may be thin, like most of the endoplasmic reticulum (p. 85) of cytoplasm, or many layers thick, as in some areas and in the grana of the chloroplasts (p 89). It is tempting to imagine that these stackings provide the large surfaces needed for the enzymatic activities of the cell and that they indicate their principal sites.

The succession of myelin sheets covering nerve fibers are, on the contrary, important for exactly the opposite reason; they are chemically nonreactive and have high electrical resistance. In sections through nerves of young animals these sheets are often clearly visible, but with age this fine structure becomes somewhat obscured through the deposition of much electron optically opaque material [31].

Muscle is the most elaborately ordered sheetlike structure to be found in nature. The electron microscope has by now revealed enough of the details of its molecular order so that we are coming very close to an understanding not merely of its macromolecular structure but of the transformations that occur in this structure as the muscle contracts and relaxes. Such molecular pictures of muscular action have already been proposed, but the available data are as yet insufficient to bring them into agreement or establish conclusively any one of them.

Like collagen, muscle was an early object for electron microscopic study. First to be examined were bits of striated muscle teased from larger masses and dried on a substrate. Photographs at low magnifications showed the system of bands made familiar by optical microscopy; those taken at higher magnifications showed each fragment as a thin, sheetlike array of macromolecular filaments lying parallel to one another and bound together by cross filaments. The parallelism is maintained along the entire fiber, and in these dried preparations the region that is anisotropic under polarized light is thicker than the rest. This earlier work with teased preparations did not establish the cause of the thickenings here or in the narrow Z band of the isotropic region. Much more is now being learned through the study of thinly sectioned muscle. The first transverse sections cut several years ago [63] demonstrated that in some regions the macromolecular filaments were regularly arranged in a hexagonal close packing. More recent studies [29] on thinner sections show that this close packing prevails throughout a muscle fiber, with more ordered fine detail in some regions than in others. The flight muscles of insects have thus far yielded the most beautiful and informative electron micrographs. In the anisotropic region of these muscles there is an especially complex molecular order. Here, but not elsewhere, a second ordered element is superimposed on the closely packed parallel array of relatively thick filaments that runs throughout the muscle. It consists of either a parallel and interlayered system of regularly distributed thinner filaments or a system of regularly distributed cross threads acting as bridges between the thicker filaments. The observations on mammalian muscle have been similar though the detail has not been so clear; they have been interpreted somewhat differently in terms of what is known about the chemical composition of muscle and what happens when muscle contracts.

Once our knowledge of functioning muscle has become reasonably complete, we will be in a position to try to see more exactly than has heretofore been possible the intimate relation that must exist between a muscle fiber and the nerves that control its activity. Much is to be learned about the mechanisms of both muscular activity and nervous stimulation by tracing these nerves to their very ends, seeing the minute structure of these endings and the exact contacts they make with elements of the muscular tissue.

Another fascinating study that becomes possible is the examination of the steps through which the developing animal synthesizes these complexly ordered structures. The orderly arrangements of the collagen macromolecules in tendon and of the macromolecules in muscle are three-dimensional though of a very different character from those of crystals. The arrangement found in muscle is even more complex than crystalline order by reason of the several molecular species it involves. It will be of more than biological significance to see how far the growth of muscle follows the pattern of crystallization made familiar by inanimate substances and to ascertain the point where the living cell intervenes in the creation of this "supercrystalline" order.

Chapter 14 | MACROMOLECULAR CRYSTALS

THE X-RAY diffraction studies of the last forty-five years have made us aware of the fact that most solids are crystalline in the sense of having their atoms and molecules in a precise and orderly three-dimensional arrangement. Among the exceptions which possess some rigidity but lack a repetitive particle order are the glasses and the gels, of which protoplasm is perhaps the most important example. In the previous chapter attention was drawn to the paracrystalline order which the electron microscope has shown in fibrous materials and which can be three-dimensional or less. The genuine crystallinity of most inanimate solids is also found in living systems, though not often except as it prevails in such inorganic constituents as teeth, shell, and bone. Though they are rare in nature, true crystals of biological substances are obtained in the laboratory from their purified preparations. The observations that can be made upon them with the electron microscope are valuable for what they can tell about fundamental questions of crystallography as well as about the substances themselves.

It is a notable fact that the occasional organic crystals observed in living organisms have usually been produced as part of a pathological process. Thus genuine but unstable crystals of the tobacco mosaic virus can be seen within infected leaves. Particles of the APC viruses (p. 116) are often tightly packed in crystalline array within the cells they infect. A crystalline product which is not the infecting agent is the so-called polyhedral body which forms within the cells of virus-diseased insects. Many nonpathological proteins present in solution in the living organism yield excellent crystals once they have been sufficiently purified in the laboratory. Their electron microscopy, in making visible the kind of ordered arrangement of elementary particles which crystallographic description has led us to expect, has been both intellectually and aesthetically satisfying. The plant virus proteins are especially rewarding in this type of study. The crystals differ markedly among themselves in outward form and perfection of particle arrangement, and thus are a rich source of information about the mechanism of crystal growth, including factors that influence the shapes they have and the faces that bound them.

Evidently to manifest crystalline array a solid must be at least a few molecules thick. Crystals of the plant virus proteins with particles 200 A or more in diameter cannot therefore be directly examined in the electron microscope. The ordered arrangement of the molecules can, however, be seen in shadowed replicas of their surfaces. The first replicas of this sort made ten years ago were of collodion, but though they did reveal molecular order they were too fragile to be widely useful. The recent substitution of evaporated carbon for collodion has removed this difficulty and made possible the investigation of many more macromolecular crystals [64]. Necessary procedures for making such crystal replicas differ very little from those already described (p. 56). They require the evaporation first of an exceedingly thin layer of shadowing metal over very minute crystals and then of a layer of carbon about 100 A thick. The resulting metal-carbon film, freed by dissolving the crystals themselves, is so thin that it will yield photographs showing high resolution. Such a replica, unlike the earlier ones of collodion, can furnish a micrograph which will reproduce the molecular order on numerous faces of a single crystal (Plates III and XIV). The arrangement that prevails within the body of the crystal is readily deduced from measurements of these distributions together with a crystallographic identification of the faces showing them. This has now been done for some virus proteins and for a number of other proteins having smaller molecules. For several the symmetry has been cubic, with a molecular arrangement that is a cubic close packing of spheres. Where the symmetry has been less, the departure from this packing has not been great. Surprisingly, no examples have been found of the equally compact hexagonal close packing.

Through application of this technique of surface reproduction to crystals having smaller and smaller molecules, there has come a recognition of the factors that limit its use. It has been uniformly successful with molecular particles as large as those of the virus proteins provided the crystals do not collapse on drying. With smaller molecules, areas of visible order have been harder to find. In only one case have they been observed on crystals with a molecular weight as low as 50,000. The faces of these smaller molecular crystals have been obscured by the larger amounts of salt needed for their formation and by the many dissolved molecules haphazardly deposited on drying. Freeing the crystalline faces from these deposits has been more difficult than might have been imagined, and no generally useful procedure for doing it has yet been found. It is this problem of getting "clean" preparations, and not the resolving power of the electron microscope, that has restricted the range of substances successfully examined.

At the present time students of the solid state of matter are as much occupied with the defects that exist in particle order as they are with the order itself. Information from the electron microscopy of these macromolecular crystals obviously bears most directly on both questions. It is now generally recognized that faults in molecular ordering, particularly of the sort designated as dislocations, can serve as foci for the growth of a crystal; the suggestion has even been made that no crystal can have a perfect particle arrangement inasmuch as without dislocations it could not have been produced. The spiral growth that proceeds from a dislocation has been seen at several scales of magnification. Coarse spirals are visible under the optical microscope [65] on the crystalline faces of such inorganic substances as silicon carbide, SiC, and cadmium iodide, CdI_2. They are beautifully demonstrated by electron micrographs of shadowed replicas of long chain hydrocarbon crystals [66]. Revealing the steps one molecule thick by which these crystals have grown, the electron micrographs permit a more intimate picture of the process than can be gained from optical examination. They have shown how growth from a single molecular dislocation results in a terracing that spirals round and round on the crystal face, while growth moving in opposite directions from multiple defects may neutralize the spiraling and yield a face composed of overlying molecular sheets of diminishing areas. Although the heights of these layers can be told from the elongated shadows cast by their edges, the threadlike molecules that make them up are too thin to have been seen individually. In the plant virus and other protein crystals, however, we see how the individual molecules are involved in these phenomena of growth. Whatever defects in molecular positions may be present in a growing crystal cannot then be overlooked.

Many hundreds of electron micrographs have now been made of protein crystals. Some are truly extraordinary in the perfection of their particle arrangement; others exhibit very clearly the predicted defects and displacements. Crystals of the southern bean mosaic virus protein are typical of those that are remarkable for the perfection of their molecular arrangement. In the hundreds that have been photographed not one has exhibited a molecular dislocation which could have served as focal

133

point for its growth (Plate III). The experience with this substance is sufficient to prove that defects of order in arrangement, common as they are in real crystals, are not necessary for their growth. The crystals of some other proteins studied have been far less perfect (Plate XV b). Those of the tobacco necrosis virus proteins, for instance, are rarely if ever free of defects. These [67] range all the way from slight misalignments of a few molecules to displacements of rows of molecules that correspond closely to the dislocations of theory and sometimes give rise to typical spirals. Often these molecular displacements do not reach below the superficial layer of molecules; in other crystals they cut across an edge and can be traced so deeply into the interior that they must have persisted throughout growth. Observations on crystals of a substance grown at different rates contribute still further to our knowledge of crystalline perfection. From this standpoint crystals of a tobacco protein formed over a period of several months have been compared with those produced instantly. Whereas the molecular order in most of the slowly formed crystals was without fault, in those rapidly grown it was so poor that individuals were always a composite of minute, badly aligned blocks. Such extreme differences in perfection are probably greater than are to be found in crystals composed of small molecules and ions, where a more active exchange undoubtedly takes place between a growing crystal and its solution.

The crystallographer finds it particularly instructive to see what the separate faces of a crystal actually look like and to try to determine if there is some obvious relation between the distributions of the molecules that constitute a face and the frequency with which different kinds of face occur. There are great differences in the molecular composition of the faces of these protein crystals. Some have their molecules closely packed to provide surfaces that are truly flat; others are defined by molecules so separated as not to contact any others lying in the plane of the face. Thus on the crystal of Plate III, the octahedral faces in the upper left and lower right corners have their molecules in tightly packed hexagonal nets; in the square net that forms the pseudocubic face shown in Plate XV a the molecules are less tightly packed but still maintain unbroken molecular contact with one another. They are the only ones in this cubic close packing in which such uninterrupted contact prevails. The solubility, which of course depends on the ease with which the particles can escape, is evidently different for each type of face and is least for those in which the molecules are most tightly bound. Octahedral and cube faces would therefore predominate on these crystals if minimum solubility were the chief factor in determining their external form. With crystals of the plant protein edestin and the liver protein ferratin this is true. These faces are, however, relatively insignificant on crystals of the southern bean mosaic virus protein though its molecules, too, are cubic close packed. Its thin, platelike crystals are dominated by a pair of dodecahedral faces (Plate III) defined by well-separated, parallel lines of molecules. Still more complicated faces are common on these crystals; thus molecules defining the face crystallographically designated as (120) and appearing here as a narrow band to the right of center do not contact one another in any direction. Obviously here we must look to factors other than minimal solubility as determining the final shape of a crystal and the faces it will manifest. With these bean mosaic crystals there are indications that their characteristic form may be ascribed to a tendency of their molecules to add themselves from solution in strings as well as one by one. More studies like this of the molecular composition of the faces on a growing crystal and of their fates as it begins to dissolve will undoubtedly help in understanding many questions dealing with the solid state.

By proper choice of conditions the examination of protein

crystals can be made to give interesting information about fundamental properties of the proteins themselves. An example of this is supplied by a comparison under the electron microscope of two types of turnip yellows virus protein crystals that are grown, in one case from alcohol, in the other from aqueous solutions rich in ammonium sulfate [68]. The arrangement in both types of crystal is a cubic close packing, but in those grown from alcohol the distance between molecular centers is nearly 50% less than in the salt-grown crystals. Evidently large amounts of salt have become part of the latter's ordered molecular array. Few, if any, proteins crystallize without some water, and the crystals of many contain as much water by weight as protein. The micrographs of the turnip yellows virus prove that crystals of a protein may have as essential ingredients large quantities of salt as well as of water. In the inorganic world the existence of hydrates has made us long ago familiar with crystals having two chemical components. These protein crystals are more complicated in having three—salt, water, and protein, all of which presumably partake in the molecular order.

In view of the difficulties in finding surfaces on protein crystals of small molecular size clean enough to expose their molecular order, it is fortunate that techniques other than surface replication exist. Some years ago electron microscopy indicated molecular order within the sectioned polyhedral bodies of insect virus disease. Now that much thinner sections can be cut this order is beautifully displayed when such polyhedra are encountered [69]. It has already been mentioned (p. 116) that many of the closely packed aggregates of the APC virus particles appear crystalline [56]. In both these instances the particles have had diameters comparable with the thickness of the section. To see order when the molecules are much smaller, two conditions must be satisfied: the crystals must be able to withstand dehydration and embedding and the sections must be so oriented that the electrons travel through them parallel to densely occupied, well-separated molecular planes. We do not yet know how often these conditions can be met.

Molecular order has recently been observed within minute intact crystals of the organic compound phthalocyanin [70]. This pigment has a molecular weight of only 514 and the composition $C_{32}N_8H_{18}$; it forms extremely thin crystals which are stable under electron bombardment. When they happen to be properly oriented with respect to the electron beam their molecular separations, of the order of 11 A, can be seen and photographed. Because these crystals are so flat the molecular order is frequently visible over relatively large areas, and this provides still another direct source of information about crystalline perfection. In a single crystal we may see regions where dislocations exist as well as large areas of perfect order. It will be especially instructive to link these occurrences with the conditions under which the crystals have grown.

The fact that existing electron microscopes have the resolving power needed to show the molecular separations in crystals built of molecules no bigger than those of phthalocyanin provides an unanticipated extension to the study of crystals. We must determine how wide a range of organic crystals can be successfully investigated in this fashion and seek new interpretations of what we see. These theoretical questions are particularly intriguing because the contrast with which molecular separations are seen and its dependence on crystal thickness indicate that interference plays a novel role in the image formation. We are beginning to visualize these small molecular separations in other substances as different as zeolites, synthetic dyestuffs (Plate XVI) and the simple inorganic compound molybdenum trioxide. These exploratory observations will gradually develop a better understanding of the kinds of crystals that should be investigated and will supply an experimental basis for the theoretical interpretation we need. Because of the requirements of thinness and stability the most fruitful observations will perhaps be made, at least for the present, on middle-sized organic molecules and a few minerals; perhaps these separations can be found when the molecules are still bigger. The visualizations of molecular order that could then be made would bridge in part the gap that now exists between simple organic crystals and the proteins of molecular weight hundreds of times greater.

Chapter 15 | CONCLUSION

THE PRECEDING CHAPTERS have been prepared to indicate the general character and some of the present content of electron microscopy considered as a typical field of specialized research. They illustrate the chief characteristics of such a specialty: a new goal in natural knowledge set by novel techniques, a characteristic preoccupation with these techniques to the exclusion of others, and a breadth of application that cuts across many of the conventional divisions of science. For electron microscopy the new goal is, as we have seen, primarily the visualization of the fine structure of matter down almost to atomic dimensions and secondarily the chemical identification and analysis of the units of structure thus revealed. The tools for reaching these goals are physical and the materials studied are sometimes inorganic and sometimes biological. Objects for examination come from many branches of natural science, and what the electron microscope tells about them bears on problems which range from the most fundamental to the most practical. Evidently the dangers of narrowness through specialization in this case at least lie not in the specialty itself but in the fact that its goals are not those of the established divisions of science.

It has been pointed out that the problem created by this difference is one of education. Acquiring skill as a specialist does not by itself give the disciplinary intellectual training essential to the development of a good scientist which can come only through the thorough mastery of some organized field of learning. Specialties do not give this training both on account of their ephemeral nature and shifting relationship to the basic sciences and because during their vigorous growth they deal with that nebulous region of the becoming-known which is so great a hazard to the untrained mind. In the adequate training of an experimental scientist a firm discipline in the basic sciences can nowadays profitably be followed by technical training in one of the specialties. Without this technical proficiency an experimentalist's contributions to knowledge will be poor in quality; without a solid and disciplined background for his work a young investigator will soon exhaust the ideas he has taken over from his elders while lacking the inner resources upon which to build his own lifelong development.

The growth of electron microscopy illustrates several of the specific problems which face a technical specialty. The most obvious of these is of course the widespread tendency to consider it only in terms of its utilitarian applications. It is unfortunate when such a subject must be developed and taught from this point of view because the significance of any specialty becomes most apparent through its use in research of a fundamental character. Such research is the work of persons of wide interests whose imaginations can play freely with the contributions the new specialty can make; and it is these potentialities as well as technical proficiency that should be taught. Only when presented in this fashion to a rising generation of scientific workers will specialties find their proper place in the totality of science. It requires repeated emphasis that technical competence is necessary to a research scientist, but both society and the young must realize that learning to be a good technician is no more than an introduction to becoming a serious student of nature. As part of the present effort to augment the scientific personnel of this country, incompletely trained persons are far too often encouraged to function as independent investigators. In doing this our society is not merely wasting its current resources but, what is far more important, is depriving itself of the infinitely more valuable services these persons could later have given if their training had not been arrested prematurely. The growth of science has amply demonstrated that fundamental research will be effectively carried out only by workers who are mature both in their technical ability and in their orientation toward problems broad enough so that they are prepared to recognize and cultivate whatever new knowledge nature may offer; and it has repeatedly shown that for most this maturity is gained only through that kind of association with the older and more experienced which we usually designate as apprenticeship.

The extensive and highly specialized literature that is a by-product of the rapid growth of electron microscopy illustrates another problem common to our mushrooming fields of specialized research. We hear much of its high cost and of the increasing difficulties that libraries have in acquiring and making available this flood of publication, but far more serious is the way it tends to restrict the interests of specialists. Largely because electron microscopy has had so little fundamental support in this country, much of the exploratory work required to define its possibilities and limitations has had to come as a by-product of its practical applications. Most of the several thousand papers published during the last ten years have dealt with such applications, and the working scientist who endeavors to command the literature of what he is doing thus finds himself spending time in the library which should be spent in the laboratory. This is less necessary when there exists the proper and useful division of a subject into its basic and utilitarian aspects.

The history of electron microscopy illustrates very clearly the price we are paying for not giving fundamental research the support it requires. During and immediately following the war most good work was carried out in the United States but even then our contributions were for the most part of a practical character. We remained dominant only as long as Europe was destitute. As soon as it again had any facilities for fundamental work it began to pull ahead, and now it once more produces both the best basic work and the best electron microscopes. The tendency in this country to treat fundamental research as a preliminary and accessory to practical work has not altered in spite of the vast amount of money now being spent. One of the many reasons for this, but an essential one, is the continuing deep-seated confusion between fundamental and applied research. It is imperative that we come to recognize and support them as separate efforts developing in their separate ways. Each has its own goal and requires a different type of mind working under a different set of conditions.

We are accustomed to distinguish between fundamental and applied research, saying that the former is the pursuit of knowledge for the sake of a better understanding of the natural world and that applied research utilizes the understanding we now have to gain more control over that world. This distinction is valid but not sufficient because fundamental research is no longer a unified effort. Until the last century our understanding of nature was so limited that most of what is now called research was exploratory. Since then a rapid succession of discoveries has opened up vast new fields of nature for future cultivation. This cultivation, needed to give body to the original exploratory findings, is fundamental research in the sense that its immediate goal is further knowledge rather than the utilization of existing knowledge. Nevertheless, it radically differs from exploration in having a goal that is clearly defined and it appeals to a totally different kind of investigator. It lends itself, for instance, to research upon a project that can be precisely described and carried out by a team of specialists. To an overwhelming extent the so-called basic research done in this country has this planned character. It is necessary; but no amount of it, no matter how successful, can replace the fundamental exploratory work which we so inadequately support and without which the other will ultimately dry up.

It is easy to understand why the organization and planning characteristic of project research should so effectively sterilize research that is exploratory. What we may hope to find through exploration cannot be given precise statement and its success cannot be assured. It is and must be the outgrowth of one man's insight, and there are relatively few in any generation who are by both ability and temperament fitted to carry it out. The conditions for life and work which these few find stimulating are usually utterly unlike those that facilitate research having a clearly defined objective. The requisite environment is simpler but is not the same for all. It has existed for limited periods in several of the institutes for basic research that have arisen and decayed over the last half century, and this past success has given practical demonstration of the conditions that must be fulfilled. We in this country must reconcile ourselves to providing them if the fundamental research we so urgently need is to flourish.

The growing complexity of natural science is producing new chapters in research besides those based on types of instrumentation. They arise where different sciences meet, and are the means of cultivating such regions which cannot be said to belong to any one science. They are more permanent than the instrumental specialties but in their early days they present many of the same problems. Among them biophysics has been most closely linked to the growth of electron microscopy. Both are based on physics, which implements electron microscopy in its investigation of the fine structure of living matter and provides biophysics with principles that can explain some of its behavior. The difference between them is, however, apparent in both their origins and their ways of development.

Electron microscopy had its start in first a discovery and then an invention that exposed a new segment of nature; it has grown through an unfolding of the knowledge thus made possible. This knowledge contributes directly to the expansion of the major sciences and will be incorporated into them. When its techniques have reached their full development and become instruments of routine investigation, they undoubtedly will be absorbed into the armory of these sciences, and electron microscopy as a specialty will probably have fulfilled its purpose.

Research which connects two basic sciences has a different history. It begins when various experimental procedures are applied to problems growing out of both and it evolves into an enduring chapter of each. Biophysics is now beginning to emerge from such origins. The most obvious has been the need of biology and medicine for help in developing and operating the increasingly complex tools required to extend our knowledge of life. This is giving many younger physicists an acquaintance with biology which their predecessors did not readily have. Fundamentally more significant, however, is the widening scope of physics itself. Classical physics arose as the study of the properties and behavior of inanimate matter. Such an initial concentration upon the inanimate substrate of existence was inevitable in view of its relative simplicity and the comparative ease with which the laws characterizing it became manifest. But it was equally inevitable that, as soon as physicists began to feel at home in this basically static order, they would become aware of the inadequacy of its laws to explain the vastly more complex phenomena presented by an organization of matter at once dynamic, ever-changing, and self-perpetuating. This movement of physical thought to include the problems of living matter has not yet developed beyond the stage of being a rather ill-defined aggregate of attempts by physicists to come to grips with some of biology's more evident problems. Biophysics will probably continue in this episodic and amorphous state until a wider appreciation of its role liberates it from its present restrictive dependence on medicine and provides it with the independent facilities essential to its natural growth.

Electron microscopy has been deeply involved in three aspects of this biophysics. One is neurophysiology. The unexpectedly intimate picture the electron microscope can give of the organizational details of the brain and its nervous extensions cannot fail to advance our knowledge of life's most complex manifestation. Another aspect of biophysics is concerned with viruses as among life's simplest manifestations. It has been pointed out how the electron microscope has already contributed otherwise unattainable knowledge of what these submicroscopic entities are and how they develop. A third chapter of biophysics includes the frank search for techniques that will provide new ways to investigate vital systems; and electron microscopy is obviously important among these.

Electron microscopy is still too young and rapidly growing to justify a guess as to how long this growth will continue. In some directions, however, the limits of its present possibilities and the directions of its further expansion are becoming apparent. Thus unless there is some quite unforeseen development the microscopes of the immediate future will not have much higher resolving powers than the best with which we now work. They will, nevertheless, be simpler and more convenient to use and we may hope that the practical lower limit to what we can examine will be extended through still better methods of specimen preparation and through control of the specimen contamination which now prevents our utilizing to the full the resolution already available. Even if such an extension were but slowly achieved the work to be done with existing instruments and techniques is so great that many years will be required to survey what can now be seen. The modification of electron microscopes to permit the microanalysis of minute areas of sample is only beginning. In this direction there will be great activity in the next few years, and it will probably be followed by widespread applications especially to inorganic materials. Perhaps with time this aspect of microscopy will become as important as its use in studying the microstructure of living systems.

The inevitable ultimate absorption of electron microscopy into biology and physical chemistry must gradually occur as the requisite instruments and the techniques for applying them become stabilized. The new cytology and histology concerned with the fine structure of cells and tissues as seen in ultrathin sections are evidence that this is already beginning to take place. How long it will be before the possible techniques of microanalysis reach a corresponding state of development will depend in part on how fruitful they prove to be. If the new information they can give about composition is as useful for a basic understanding of the properties of solids as is the electron microscope's new information about their microstructure, this development may require a number of years. In any event it is clear that the microscope and its associated techniques have now grown to the point where their adequate utilization depends on the rapidity with which they are absorbed into biology and chemistry and taught as a fruitful means of extending the boundaries of these sciences. To this extent electron microscopy already illustrates the complete life history of an instrumental specialty.

REFERENCES

THE BIBLIOGRAPHIC REFERENCES of this book are illustrative only. They include no papers published before 1950 and only those more recent articles which are particularly pertinent to the subjects discussed or will provide a starting point for a more detailed study of these subjects.

1. For advanced discussions of electron microscopy in English, see:
V. K. Zworykin, G. A. Morton, E. G. Ramberg, J. Hillier, and A. W. Vance. Electron Optics and the Electron Microscope. New York, 1945.
C. E. Hall, Introduction to Electron Microscopy. New York, 1953.

2. See for instance:
W. Ehrenberg and W. E. Spear, Nature, 168, 513 (1951).
V. E. Cosslett and W. C. Nixon, Nature, 170, 436 (1952).
W. C. Nixon, Proc. Roy. Soc., 232 A, 475 (1955); Brit. J. Radiology, 28, 532 (1955).
A. Engström, Physiological Reviews, 33, 190 (1953); Exper. Cell Res. Suppl. 3, 117 (1955); A. Engström and L. Wegstedt, Acta Radiologica, 35, 345 (1951); B. Combée and A. Engström, Biochim. et Biophys. Acta, 14, 432 (1954).

3. Electron microscopes in use in this country are manufactured and sold by the following companies:
Philips Electronics, Inc., Mount Vernon, N.Y.
RCA-Victor Division, Camden, N.J.
Siemens & Halske AG, Berlin

Other models are manufactured and sold in Europe and in Japan.

4. P. Chanson and C. Magnan, Compt. rend., 233, 1436 (1951); 238, 1701, 1797 (1954).

5. H. Boersch, Experientia 4, 1 (1948); M. Gauzit, Compt. rend., 233, 1586 (1951); G. Couchet, M. Gauzit and A. Septier, Compt. rend., 233, 1087 (1951); Bull. Micr. Appl. 2, 85 (1952).

6. E. W. Müller, Z. Physik, 131, 136 (1951); J. Applied Physics, 27, 474 (1956).
J. A. Becker, Tech. J. Bell System, 30, 907 (1951).
M. Drechsler and E. W. Müller, Metall., 6, 341 (1952); M. Drechsler, Z. physik. Chem., 6, 272 (1956).
D. J. Rose, J. Applied Physics, 27, 215 (1956).

7. For years the Electron Microscope Society of America maintained a bibliographic service under the general supervision of Perry Smith; this is being continued by the New York Society of Electron Microscopists. References to early work (before 1950) dealing with many of the subjects discussed in this book can also be found in the writer's Electron Microscopy, Technique and Applications, New York, Interscience Publishers, 1949. Literature reviews for recent years will be found in:
M. Swerdlow, Anal. Chem., 26, 34 (1954); M. Swerdlow, A. J. Dalton and L. S. Birks, Anal. Chem., 28, 597 (1956).

8. L. Robert, J. Bussot and J. Buzon, 1er Cong. Intern. Microscopie Electronique (Paris, 1950), p. 528.
D. E. Bradley, Brit. J. Appl. Phys. 5, 65, 96 (1954); 6, 430 (1955); J. Inst. Metals, 83, 35 (1954).

9. T. F. Anderson, Biol. Bull., 99, 315 (1950); 1er Cong. Intern. Microscopie Electronique (Paris, 1950), pp. 567, 577.

10. A. Policard, A. Collet, and L. Ralyte, Compt. rend., 235, 224 (1952); 236, 1458 (1953); 239, 1149 (1954); 240, 2473 (1955); Rev. d'hématol., 9, 402 (1954); 10, 3, 674 (1955).

G. Pfefferkorn, Arch. Hyg., *135*, 14 (1951); *138*, 599 (1954); Z. Aerosol Forsch., *4*, 531 (1955).

L. Dautrebande, Essai de prévention de la silicose, 1954. Published by Union Minière du Haut-Katanga; contains extensive bibliography.

11. D. B. Scott and R. W. G. Wyckoff, Jour. Roy. Micros. Soc. *75*, 217 (1955).

12. For a review, see D. B. Scott, Intern. Dental Jour., *4*, 64 (1953).

13. C. Fert and R. Saporte, Compt. rend., *235*, 1490 (1952); C. Fert and B. Marty, Compt. rend., *241*, 1454 (1955).
M. E. Haine and W. Hirst, Brit. J. Appl. Phys., *4*, 239 (1953).
J. A. Chapman and J. W. Menter, Proc. Roy. Soc., *226* A, 400 (1954).
V. E. Cosslett and D. Jones, J. Sci. Instr., *32*, 86 (1955); D. Jones, Bull. Inst. Metals, *2*, 235 (1955).
K. Ito, T. Ito, and M. Watanabe, J. Electron Microscopy (Japan) *2*, 10 (1954).

14. C. Fert, B. Marty, and R. Saporte, Compt. rend., *240*, 1975 (1955); Les Techniques récentes en microscopie électronique (Colloque du CNRS, Toulouse, 1955), p. 91.

15. L. Mayer, J. Applied Physics, *26*, 1228 (1955).

16. G. W. Rathenau and G. Baas, Physica, *17*, 117 (1951); Métaux, *29*, 139 (1954).
See also:
R. J. Ueda, Electron Microscopy (Japan), *1*, 42 (1953).
A. Septier and M. Gauzit, 1er Cong. Intern. Microscopie Electronique (Paris, 1950), p. 246.

17. G. W. Rathenau and G. Baas, in reference (16).

18. G. Möllenstedt and H. Düker, Optik, *10*, 192 (1953); G. Möllenstedt and W. Hubig, Optik, *11*, 528 (1954).

A. M. Septier, Compt. rend., 237, 231 (1953).

19. D. McMullan, Proc. Inst. Elect. Engin., 75, 245 (1953).
K. C. A. Smith and C. W. Oatley, Brit. J. Appl. Phys., 6, 391 (1955).

20. V. E. Cosslett and W. C. Nixon, in reference (2)
V. M. Mosley, D. B. Scott, and R. W. G. Wyckoff, in press.

21. V. M. Mosley, D. B. Scott, and R. W. G. Wyckoff, Science, 124, 683 (1956); Biochim. et Biophys. Acta, 24, 235 (1957).

22. H. Latta and J. F. Hartmann, Proc. Soc. Exp. Biol. Med., 74, 436 (1950).

23. The special microtomes for electron microscopy most familiar to American workers are the Porter-Blum (Anat. Record, 117, 685 [1953]) and Sjöstrand (Z. wiss. Mikroskop., 62, 65 [1954]) designs, both of which are supplied by Ivan Sorvall, Inc., Norwalk, Conn.
A simple way of modifying the Spencer rotary microtome for thin-sectioning and a bibliography of other instruments are to be found in M. Nylen and J. W. Holland, Jr., Exp. Cell Research, 13, 88 (1957).

24. G. G. Cocks and C. M. Schwartz, Rev. Sci. Instr., 23, 615 (1952).
H. B. Haanstra, Philips Tech. Rev., 17, 178 (1955).
S. Claesson and A. A. Svensson, Exp. Cell Research, 11, 114 (1956).

25. O. Maaløe and A. Birch-Andersen, 6th Symposium of Soc. Gen. Microbiology (Cambridge, 1956), p. 261.

26. For instance:
G. E. Palade and K. R. Porter, J. Exp. Med., 100, 641 (1954); G. E. Palade, J. Biophys. Biochem. Cytology, 1, 59, 567 (1955).

A. J. Dalton and M. D. Felix, Am. J. Anat., 94, 171 (1954).

M. L. Watson, Biochim. et Biophys. Acta, 15, 475 (1954).

27. For instance:
F. S. Sjöstrand and V. Hanzon, Exp. Cell Research, 7, 393, 415 (1954).

28. For instance:
F. S. Sjöstrand, J. Cell. Comp. Physiol., 42, 45 (1953).

M. A. Jakus, Am. J. Opthalmol., 38, 40 (1954); J. Biophys. Biochem. Cytology, 2, 241 (1956).

E. De Robertis, J. Biophys. Biochem. Cytology, 2, 319 (1956); E. De Robertis and C. M. Franchi, in ibid., 2, 307 (1956).

H. Engström and J. Wersall, Acta Oto-Laryngol., 43, 1, 323 (1953); H. Engström and F. S. Sjöstrand, in ibid., 44, 490 (1954).

29. M. H. Draper and A. J. Hodge, Aust. J. Exp. Biol. Med. Sci., 27, 465 (1949); A. J. Hodge, J. Biophys. Biochem. Cytology, 1, 361 (1955); A. J. Hodge, H. E. Huxley, and D. Spiro, J. Exp. Med., 99, 201 (1954); H. E. Huxley, Biochim. et Biophys. Acta, 12, 387 (1953); D. Spiro, Exp. Cell Research, 10, 562 (1956).

J. L. Farrant and E. H. Mercer, Exp. Cell Research, 3, 553 (1952).

G. B. Chapman, J. Morph., 95, 237 (1954).

H. S. Bennett and K. R. Porter, Am. J. Anatomy, 93, 61 (1953).

F. S. Sjöstrand and E. Andersson, Experientia, 10, 369 (1954).

D. E. Philpott and A. Szent-Györgyi, Biochim. et Biophys. Acta, 18, 177 (1955); D. E. Philpott, Biol. Bull., 107, 302 (1954).

30. For instance:
J. D. Robertson, Exp. Cell Research 8, 226 (1955); J. Biophys. Biochem. Cytology, 1, 271 (1955).

S. L. Palay and G. Palade, J. Biophys. Biochem. Cytology, *1*, 69 (1955).

E. De Robertis and S. H. Bennett, Anat. Record Suppl., *118*, 294 (1954); J. Biophys. Biochem. Cytology, 1, 47 (1955).

R. W. G. Wyckoff and J. Z. Young, Proc. Roy. Soc., *144 B*, 440 (1956).

J. F. Hartmann, J. Comp. Neurol., 99, 201 (1953); Anat. Record, *118*, 19 (1954).

E. W. Dempsey and G. B. Wislocki, J. Biophys. Biochem. Cytology, 1, 111, 245 (1955).

S. A. Luse, J. Biophys. Biochem. Cytology, 2, 531, 777 (1956).

31. H. Fernandez-Moran, Exp. Cell Research, 1, 143, 309 (1950); 3, 282 (1952); 4, 480 (1953).

F. S. Sjöstrand, Nature, *165*, 482 (1950); Experientia, 9, 68 (1953); J. B. Finean, F. S. Sjöstrand, and E. Steinmann, Exp. Cell Research, 5, 557 (1953).

32. For instance:

J. D. Robertson, J. Biophys. Biochem. Cytology, 2, 369, 381 (1956).

J. F. Reger, Anat. Record, *118*, 275 (1954); 122, 1 (1955).

E. De Robertis, J. Biophys. Biochem. Cytology, 2, 503 (1956).

A. Hess and A. I. Lansing, Anat. Record, *117*, 175 (1953).

33. E. Steinmann, Exp. Cell Research, 3, 367 (1952); 8, 15 (1955).

R. Sager and G. E. Palade, Exp. Cell Research, 7, 584 (1954).

H. Leyon, Exp. Cell Research, 4, 371; 5, 520 (1953); 7, 265 (1954).

K. Mühlethaler, Intern. Rev. Cytology, 4, 197 (1955).

F. V. Mercer, A. J. Hodge, A. B. Hope, and J. D. McLean, Austr. J. Biol. Sci., 8, 1 (1955).

34. F. C. Steward and K. Mühlethaler, Ann. Botany, 17, 295 (1953).

R. D. Preston and G. W. Ripley, Nature, 174, 76 (1954); R. D. Preston and B. Kuyper, J. Exp. Botany, 2, 247 (1951).

K. Wilson, Ann. Botany, 15, 279 (1951).

A. B. Wardrop, Austr. J. Botany, 2, 154 (1954).

35. S. M. Mukherjee, J. Sikorski, and H. J. Woods, J. Textile Inst., 43, 196 (1952); S. M. Mukherjee, and H. J. Woods, Biochim. et Biophys. Acta, 10, 499 (1953).

V. Balashov and R. D. Preston, Nature, 176, 64 (1955).

B. G. Ranby, Makromol. Chem., 13, 40 (1954).

36. I. Manton, Nature, 171, 485 (1953); 176, 123 (1955); I. Manton, B. Clarke, and A. D. Greenwood, J. Exp. Botany, 4, 319 (1953); 6, 126 (1955).

D. W. Fawcett, Laryngoscope, 64, 557 (1954).

B. P. Potts and S. G. Tomlin, Biochim. et Biophys. Acta, 16, 66 (1955).

37. M. H. Burgos and D. W. Fawcett, J. Biophys. Biochem. Cytology, 1, 287 (1955); 2, 223 (1956).

38. G. Rozsa and R. W. G. Wyckoff, Biochem. et Biophys. Acta, 6, 334 (1950); Exp. Cell Research, 2, 630 (1951).

A. W. Sedar and D. F. Wilson, Biol. Bull., 100, 107 (1951).

E. Borysko, Bull. Johns Hopkins Hosp., 92, 151 (1953).

D. W. Fawcett, J. Biophys. Biochem. Cytology, 2, 403 (1956).

39. R. F. Sognnaes, D. B. Scott, M. J. Ussing, and R. W. G. Wyckoff, J. Dental Res., 31, 85 (1952).

40. A. L. Houwink, Biochim. et Biophys. Acta, 10, 360 (1953).

L. W. Labaw and V. M. Mosley, J. Bact., 67, 576 (1954); Biochim. et Biophys. Acta, 15, 325 (1954).

153

M. P. Starr and R. C. Williams, J. Bact., *63*, 701 (1952).

I. M. Dawson and H. Stern, Biochim. et Biophys. Acta, *13*, 31 (1954).

N. Yoshida, I. Kakutani, I. Fukuya, and S. Tanaka, J. Electron Microscopy (Japan), *3*, 52 (1955).

41. A. Birch-Andersen, O. Maaløe, and F. S. Sjöstrand, Biochim. et Biophys. Acta, *12*, 395 (1953); A. Birch-Andersen, J. Gen. Microbiol., *13*, 327 (1955).

S. G. Tomlin and J. W. May, Austr. J. Exp. Biol. Med. Sci., *33*, 249 (1955).

42. F. Weyer and D. Peters, Z. Naturforsch., *7b*, 357 (1952).

K. Liebermeister, Z. Naturforsch., *8b*, 757 (1953).

H. E. Morton, J. G. Lecce, J. J. Oskay, and N. H. Coys, J. Bact., *68*, 697 (1954).

E. Kleineberger-Nobel and F. W. Cuckow, J. Gen. Biol., *12*, 95 (1955); J. Gen. Microbiol., *13*, 149 (1955).

43. V. Cosentino, K. Paigen, and R. L. Steere, Virology, *2*, 139 (1956).

44. L. M. Black, C. Morgan, and R. W. G. Wyckoff, Proc. Soc. Exp. Biol. Med., *73*, 119 (1950).

H. Leyon, Exp. Cell Research, *4*, 362 (1953).

C. B. Skotland, D. J. Hagedorn, and M. A. Stahmann, Phytopath., *45*, 603 (1955).

J. Brandes, Phytopath. Z., *26*, 93 (1956).

45. D. Fraser and R. C. Williams, J. Bact., *65*, 167; *66*, 458 (1953).

H. Noda, Biochim. et Biophys. Acta, *12*, 495 (1953).

46. T. F. Anderson, J. Applied Phys., *21*, 70 (1950).

A. D. Hershey and M. Chase, J. Gen. Physiol., *36*, 39 (1952).

47. V. Bonifas and E. Kellenberger, Biochim. et Biophys. Acta, *16*, 330 (1955).

48. O. Maaløe, A. Birch-Andersen, and F. S. Sjöstrand, Biochim. et Biophys. Acta, 15, 12 (1954).

49. R. W. G. Wyckoff and B. E. Eddy, Proc. Soc. Exp. Biol. Med., 75, 290 (1950); R. W. G. Wyckoff, Nature, 168, 651 (1951); J. Immun., 70, 187 (1953).
J. S. Murphy and F. B. Bang, J. Exp. Med., 95, 259 (1952).
C. Morgan, H. M. Rose, and D. H. Moore, J. Exp. Med., 104, 171 (1956).
C. G. Harford, A. Hamlin, and E. Parker, J. Exp. Med., 101, 577 (1955).

50. L. Kilham, C. Morgan, and R. W. G. Wyckoff, J. Immunol., 67, 523 (1951).
F. B. Bang, Bull. Johns Hopkins Hosp., 92, 291 (1953).

51. P. Lépine and O. Croissant, Bull. Microscop. Appl., 5, 22 (1955).

52. R. W. G. Wyckoff, Proc. Nat. Acad. Sci., 37, 565 (1951); Z. Zellforsch. 38, 409 (1953).
W. H. Gaylord, Jr., and J. L. Melnick, J. Exp. Med., 98, 157 (1953).
C. Morgan, S. A. Ellison, H. M. Rose, and D. H. Moore, Exp. Cell Research, 9, 572 (1955).

53. C. Morgan, S. A. Ellison, H. M. Rose, and D. H. Moore, Proc. Soc. Exp. Biol. Med., 82, 454 (1953).
M. Reissig and J. L. Melnick, J. Exp. Med., 101, 341 (1955).
R. W. G. Wyckoff, O. Croissant, and P. Lépine, Ann. Inst. Pasteur, 90, 18 (1956).

54. H. L. Bachrach and C. E. Schwerdt, J. Immunol., 72, 30 (1954).
H. Ruska, D. C. Stuart, and J. Winsser, Arch. ges. Virusforsch., 6, 379 (1955).
P. Lépine, O. Croissant, and R. W. G. Wyckoff, Ann. Inst. Pasteur, 90, 13 (1956).

55. K. M. Smith, Proc. Roy. Soc., *142* B, 196 (1954); K. M. Smith, and R. W. G. Wyckoff, Research, *4*, 148 (1951).

K. M. Hughes, Hilgardia, *22*, 391 (1953).

C. Vago, O. Croissant, and P. Lépine, Ann. Inst. Pasteur, *89*, 364 (1955).

56. C. G. Harford, A. Hamlin, E. Parker, and T. van Ravenswaay, J. Exp. Med., *104*, 443 (1956); C. Morgan, C. Howe, H. M. Rose, and D. H. Moore, J. Biophys. Biochem. Cytology, *2*, 351 (1956).

57. G. A. Hottle, C. Morgan, J. H. Peers, and R. W. G. Wyckoff, Proc. Soc. Exp. Biol. Med., *77*, 721 (1951).

O. Croissant, P. Lépine, and R. W. G. Wyckoff, Ann. Inst. Pasteur, *89*, 183 (1955).

58. J. L. Farrant, Biochim. et Biophys. Acta, *13*, 569 (1954).

59. D. Fraser and R. C. Williams, Proc. Nat. Acad. Sci., *39*, 750 (1953).

H. Kahler and B. J. Lloyd, Jr., Biochim. et Biophys. Acta, *10*, 355 (1953).

C. E. Hall, J. Biophys. Biochem. Cytology, *2*, 625 (1956).

60. G. F. Bahr, Exp. Cell Research, *1*, 603 (1950); *3*, 485 (1952).

H. Noda and R. W. G. Wyckoff, Biochim. et Biophys. Acta, *7*, 494 (1951).

J. H. Highberger, J. Gross, and F. O. Schmitt, Proc. Nat. Acad. Sci., *37*, 286 (1951); *39*, 459 (1953); *41*, 1 (1955).

61. R. W. G. Wyckoff, 3rd Conf. Connective Tissues (Macy Foundation) (1952), p. 38.

62. D. E. Philpott and A. C. Szent-Györgyi, Biochim. et Biophys. Acta, *15*, 165 (1954).

63. C. Morgan, G. Rozsa, A. Szent-Györgyi, and R. W. G. Wyckoff, Science, *111*, 201 (1950).

64. L. W. Labaw and R. W. G. Wyckoff, Nature, 176, 455 (1955); Exp. Cell Research Suppl., 3, 395 (1955); Koninkl. Nederl. Akad. Amsterdam, 59 B, 171 (1956).

65. See W. Dekeyser and S. Amelinckx, Les Dislocations et la croissance des cristaux, Paris, 1955.

A. R. Verma, Crystal Growth and Dislocations, London, 1953.

66. I. M. Dawson, Nature, 168, 241 (1951); Proc. Roy. Soc., 214 A, 72 (1952); I. M. Dawson and V. Vand, Nature, 167, 476 (1951); Proc. Roy. Soc., 206 A, 555 (1951); N. G. Anderson and I. M. Dawson, Proc. Roy. Soc., 218 A, 255 (1953); 228 A, 539 (1955).

67. R. W. G. Wyckoff and L. W. Labaw, Les Techniques récentes en microscopie électronique (Colloque du CNRS, Toulouse, 1955), p. 135.

68. L. W. Labaw and R. W. G. Wyckoff, Science, 123, 849 (1956).

69. C. Morgan, G. H. Bergold, D. H. Moore, and H. M. Rose, J. Biophys. Biochem. Cytology, 1, 187 (1955); 2, 23 (1956).

70. J. W. Menter, Proc. Roy. Soc., 236 A, 119 (1956); L. W. Labaw and R. W. G. Wyckoff, Koninkl. Nederl. Akad. Amsterdam, 59 B, 449 (1956).

INDEX

Aberrations, *see* Image defects

Absorption of electrons in electron microscopy, 24

Actin molecules, electron microscopy of, 126

Adeno viruses: development of, 116; crystal-like packing of, 136

Albumin, use of, in freeze-drying particulate suspensions, 44

Aluminum films as specimen supports, 41; as shadowing layers for optical microscopy, 54

Aluminum oxide replicas, 54

APC viruses, *see* Adeno viruses

Astigmatism in electron lenses: correction for, 29; definition, 29

Bacteria, electron microscopy of, 94; after sectioning, 95

Bacterial nuclei, existence of, 95

Bacteriophage development: electron microscopy of, 105 ff.; mechanism of, 108

Bacteriophage particles: fine structure of, 100; for T strains against E. coli, 105; internal structure of, 106

Barium film in emission electron microscopy, 64

Bean mosaic virus, *see* Southern bean mosaic virus

Beryllium films as specimen supports, 41

Bibliography of electron microscopy, 147 ff.

Biophysics: relation of electron microscopy to, 143; general character of, 144

Brain, electron microscopy of, 86 ff.

Brownian motion: limitation on effective resolution set by, 36; desiccation of specimen to arrest, 37

Cancer, relation to viruses, 118

Carbon, evaporated films: as specimen support, 41; as replicas, 53

Cathode rays, *see* Electrons

Cellulose, electron microscopy of, 89

Cesium film in emission electron microscopy, 63

Chloroplasts, electron microscopy of, 89

Chorioallantoic membranes, electron microscopy of virus-diseased c.m., 104

Chromatic aberrations in electron microscopes, 28; effect of specimen thickness on, 29

Chromium films as shadowing layers, 42 f.

Chromosomes, electron microscopy of, 92

Clays: examination of, by combined electron microscopy and diffraction, 50; replicas of, 53

Coherent scattering of electrons, 24

Collagen: electron microscopy of c. fibers, 123; reprecipitated, 124; several forms of, 124

Collodion membranes: as specimen supports, 40; method of preparing, 40; as replicas for electron microscopy, 53; as replicas for op-

159